MAN OF GALILEE

MAN OF GALILEE

FREDERICK PELSER

I humbly dedicate this book to the One of whom Pilate said, 'Behold the Man!'

*Sincerest appreciation
to Ernest Marter, who
opened Hebrew and the
deeper delectations of
hermeneutics to me.*

EDITOR
DAVID MARSHALL

*All Bible translations from the Greek, Hebrew and
Aramaic are by the author*

ISBN 1-873796-28-5

CONTENTS

He hardly heard John's admiring, 'Look! A city of tents!'

Behind him was Jerusalem; ahead, Gethsemane. The pilgrims from far and near lay asleep in their tents, but for him all thought of sleep was banished by Gethsemane.

In the full moon under those olive trees he had spent happy nights, enriching nights. But he now felt repelled. By going into that garden tonight, he was walking into the jaws of death.

Minutes earlier he had pointed out a sprawling grapevine and launched into a lively, earnest conversation. Now he was silent.

At the gate the twelve men halted and John's voice was strained. 'Master, why are you suddenly so sad, so . . . '

'I'm sorry,' he said. 'I feel . . . weighed down with sorrow. I feel I could die.'

He clutched his forehead and swayed.

'What . . . !'

Peter and John had their arms about him. He groaned and gradually pulled himself together.

'John, Peter, James — will you come with me? The rest of you, will you stay here — in prayer?'

Near the middle of the garden he said to the three, 'This is where you will stay. Pray with me, as you've never prayed before!'

He wanted their company, yet did not want them to see his suffering. A little distance farther on, not beyond sight and sound of them, he went down at full length.

He shuddered, but not because death was only hours away.

Something infinitely more dreadful faced him. A black void was yawning at his feet, ready to swallow him for ever. Never could he land in it by accident . . . he would have to walk into it, surrender himself to it.

The three men heard his groans and yearned to rush to

his side. But he had wanted a vestige of privacy; so they prayed on fervently, uncomprehendingly.

Nearly an hour passed. While the three and the other eight fell asleep he prayed, tormented by a temptation to get up and walk out of the garden, out of the lives of those pilgrims in their tents, those men and women in Jerusalem — everybody's life. It would be so easy!

Wet with dew, he clung to the cold ground as though to keep from being sucked into the black abyss, while waves of faintness swept over him.

'Father!' he cried. 'If it is at all possible, let this thing pass me by!'

His hand trembled across his forehead, and in the bright moonlight he saw his fingers streaked with blood . . .

A LIGHT SHINES

The shepherds of Bethlehem seemed far away at this moment . . . thirty-three years that seemed an eternity.

The angels had hunted high and low for someone ready to welcome the Messiah. At the temple the prayers and even the rites pointing to his coming, such as the morning and evening sacrifice, had become empty ceremonies. The chosen people were indifferent to the coming of the one who could save them, absorbed in material things and a religion that had lost its heart.

Then the angels found a handful of simple folk, shepherds, watching over their flocks in the summery night near Bethlehem . . . and *they* were talking longingly about the Messiah! They talked for an hour or two, and prayed that he might come soon.

An angel revealed himself to them in a burst of light, and they shrank back with cries of fear.

'Do not be afraid! I bring you good news, joyous news

for every human being. Just born to you in David's city is a Saviour, Christ the Lord!'

He had to prepare them for the humble circumstances the Messiah had chosen to mark his coming to planet Earth, and added, 'This is what you must look for: a baby wrapped in swaddling bands, lying in a manger.'

The host of angels waiting above the hills of Bethlehem turned the whole plain bright as day as they sang, 'Glory to God in the highest, and on earth peace for all who do his will!'

Then the brilliant light was gone, leaving in the shepherds' memories the brightest picture ever beheld by human eyes.

They rushed to the village and made their way up and down the rows of dark buildings until they saw a glow of light from a stable door . . .

Meanwhile, in their restless search for truth some wise men in the East had got hold of the sacred writings of Israel. Here they came across more than human wisdom. They were particularly impressed by the prophecies about the coming Seed of the woman, the one whose past stretched back into 'the days of eternity' — yet he was to be born on earth! Gathering clue upon clue, they could eventually think and talk of nothing but the predicted 'Star' that would rise in a distant land.

So rare and precious are truth-hungry, God-seeking hearts, that heaven decided to send these men a 'star' to guide them to Bethlehem. One night while others slept they saw the pulsing light, saw it move, hesitate as if beckoning, move again. In great excitement they got ready for a long journey. They had no trouble following the light even to small villages above which it paused. Had it been at a great distance in outer space, there would have been no following it to one village out of many. But the cluster of bright angels, like those who flooded Bethlehem's plain with light, moved close to earth, and moved only at a pace that men could follow.

'The star is hovering over Jerusalem!' they exclaimed at last, early one morning. 'Right over the temple!'

They hurried to the city, eagerly asking at the holy place where the newborn King was. Mocking smiles greeted their heathen ignorance — everyone knew that no royal birth had taken place.

They were so persistent that the news reached King Herod. Startled and worried, he called in the priests and wanted to know what their sacred books taught about the place of the Messiah's birth. Their efforts to shrug off the question infuriated him. Cowed by his anger, they admitted that the prophet Micah had named Bethlehem.

Herod summoned the wise men from the East and listened to their story about the star which was no longer visible.

'When did you first see it?' he asked, and made a note of the date. 'This is wonderful news! You men must do your best to find the child. Let me know where he is. I can't wait to go and worship him myself!'

That evening they again saw the light, and followed it to Bethlehem. To their intense surprise, it led them to a stable, poor working-class parents, and a baby in a manger.

THE BLIND PRIEST 3

The bored priest took the baby, aged about six weeks, in his arms and held it up before the altar. The parents were poor, so he paid them scant attention and hurried through the ceremony.

'Your first-born?' he asked the mother, and she nodded eagerly. 'Name?'

'Yeshua,' said the father in Aramaic.

Having taken the ransom money for the boy, the priest

scribbled the name 'Jesus' in the temple roll of the first-born and reached for the next baby.

But, with all heaven looking on, the event was not to pass without recognition. An elderly man named Simeon had been watching. A humble layman, he lived the divine life. Impressed by the Holy Spirit, he pushed past the priest, took the baby from the mother and presented him before God.

'Now I'm ready to die, Lord!' he exclaimed. 'You promised I would see this day. Now my eyes have seen your salvation! The light has dawned for all people and nations, including Israel!'

Prophetically, in words that would haunt the parents, he added, 'Because of this child many in Israel will fall, then rise again. He will be a sign which men will reject, thereby showing what their real character is. And the day will come when a sword will pierce his mother's heart.'

An old woman named Anna, a prophetess, added her voice in praise, and in faith that she had seen the Saviour.

The priest did not approve of these eccentric outbursts, and the rest of Jerusalem went its own way.

AWAKENING 4

Gold, frankincense and myrrh had been left behind as gifts by the wise men, overwhelming the simple parents to whom this was undreamed-of wealth. There was divine purpose behind the gifts. When the wise Easterners bypassed Jerusalem on their return journey, having been warned in a divine dream, Herod grew desperate and decided to use force to make sure no child could survive who might lay claim to his throne. Soldiers were dispatched to kill those children in Bethlehem who were under 2 years of age. The town was to be plunged in horror and mourning.

An angel appeared to Joseph, telling him to take Mary

and the child and flee to Egypt. The money needed for the journey and life in a strange country would have come from the wise men's gifts.

Soon Herod, so intent on retaining his power, lost his life. Told by an angel to return to Israel, Joseph found Herod's cruel and capricious son Archelaus ruler in Judea. Under divine guidance he settled in Nazareth, his former home.

Some day people would speak of those Nazareth years as 'quiet' and 'uneventful'. That was not how the boy Jesus found them. They were years of awakening and a never-ending struggle of extreme danger, perseverance . . . and joy.

In his adopted human nature, Jesus's first recollections were of his mother's voice as she told him stories from the Scriptures and prayed for him. He was often tugging at her skirts for more, and she unfailingly drew him closer and had a new story or text ready.

As his vocabulary increased he had endless questions, particularly about Moses and Isaiah and their writings, and about those men of exemplary life, Joseph and Daniel. The rhythms of thought in the Psalms held a special appeal for him, and he repeated portions after his parents until the words were embedded in his memory.

His parents were not always ready with an answer to his questions. This forced them to go to the synagogue school to ply the rabbis with their son's questions, and on occasion he was taken along to be the ignored witness to the replies. Some of those replies were confusingly long, full of human traditions; yet the parents seemed impressed.

Life was busy. Because of their poverty and the great deal of work that had to be done daily, the boy was given his share of jobs from his earliest years — sweeping, fetching, carrying, tending to the fire, helping in his father's workshop, doing clean-up tasks for his mother. He was always glad to do the work given him, because he could see it lightened the load on his parents.

Playing with children his age was an adventure. He enjoyed the games because they briefly made him part of a world his own size.

While they ran, jumped, climbed trees, balanced on beams and tossed stones at circles they had drawn in the ground, he learned that the children of Nazareth were not angels. He would remember the impeccable Daniel and his three young friends, and Joseph sold as a slave to Egypt . . . and sadly look around in vain for such a character among them.

His mother was gradually teaching him to read and write — a marvellous world to explore. They were too poor, however, to own any books. He was particularly eager to see, and touch, and read the Scriptures.

'When you start school at the synagogue you'll have that chance — not before,' his mother told him.

At morning and evening worship his father presided as priest in their home. He was dignified and serious, his strong voice gentle.

On these solemn yet joyful occasions they sang a good deal. This charmed the boy's mind. Singing was as natural as breathing, he thought. His heart was glad — wasn't he blessed with good peasant parents, good simple food, a humble home, the chance to serve in home and workshop, the privilege of worship? — and this gladness flowed out in psalms and heavenly songs. Sometimes his father would be working at the bench with a worried frown on his face, but when his little assistant started singing his eyes would twinkle, his face relax.

As the day neared when he should start school, he grew perplexed. He had gained some impressions of the school. There was a lot of noisy memorizing, but when he had paused to listen to the words he had recognized no Scripture. There was a jumble of sound from ritual prayers. The children seemed to be involved in a great deal of ceremony. He had heard history being presented, with emphasis on the

13

greatness of his people and the decadence of all other nations. There was sacred music, but it somehow had a doleful sound. They seemed very, very hard at work getting their minds full of things that did not appeal to him.

His mind was too immature to analyse his impressions, but he knew he was unhappy with the prospect of becoming part of the blabbing and ceremonial bustle of the school. He sought his parents' wisdom in the matter. They did not understand the school, but stood in awe of it and expected it to do great things for him. He determined to ask God.

He had been gaining progressively greater freedom in prayer, so that he did not need the crutches of set forms and phrases but talked with God as with an infinitely exalted and tender Father. He felt at home with this kind of prayer. As part of prayer he found that meditation gave him a wonderful feeling of God's presence.

In the matter of school going, he sensed a special need of God's wisdom and guidance, and explained to his parents that he needed time for a personal experience in God. A significant look passed between them. His father said nothing, but his mother encouraged him with a gentle smile. He began to spend several hours each day in prayer on a hillside.

He thought of Elijah who did not find God in the hurricane that smashed the rocks on the mountains, nor in the earthquake, nor the fire; but did find him in the still small voice. And one day he went back to the synagogue school and stood there, looking, listening. A great sadness came over him. Nowhere in this was there the still small voice of personal experience in God. Here the accent was on externals. They were studying hard, cramming their minds full of . . . of what? Things considered necessary for the material life and the spiritual life, all mixed with human wisdom and tradition. It seemed to him they were honest and trying hard, but were learning about God rather than from God.

Back in his place of prayer it became clear to him that the synagogue school, well-intentioned as the idea behind it was, was not for him. It would spoil something in him. It would hold down the powers of the soul, produce a narrowness of vision, shorten mental horizons.

This insight, he knew instinctively, was not the product of his developing little mind. It was from God, who had answered his prayers. He now knew that he must not attend school — not for a single day. He must have access to the Scriptures kept in the school; God must be his teacher.

To get his parents to understand this proved impossible. He tried in every tactful way. His father was unhappy at his wish for self-education, and his mother was sad. They looked pensively at each other and discussed the matter when alone. The father could, as undisputed leader of the home, have plunged the boy in great distress by ordering him to attend the school; but he decided to leave him to his own choice. It was a passing phase, this aversion to school. He would get out of it when he saw what progress his friends were making. Peer pressure would change his mind.

He worked harder than ever to help his parents, cheer them, and show his love for them.

Being already able to read and write, he obtained permission to spend time every afternoon with the Scriptures at the synagogue school. The authorities could not really be bothered with him, so long as he kept out of their way and did no damage. He worked hard for money to buy pieces of papyrus, and copied sections of the Scriptures for himself.

To be delving into the sacred writings was the most thrilling and exalted experience of his life. And when he came across certain prophetic passages he could not turn away. Even when he set eyes on them for the first time, there was the feeling of closeness about them, a familiar look such as a mirror brings.

Besides increasing his understanding of God, his understanding of mankind, and his understanding of himself, the Scriptures were daily adding to his vocabulary and linguistic ability. This especially improved his Hebrew; and because of the similarities between Hebrew and the Aramaic of daily speech, his use of his mother tongue grew more facile by the day, surprising his parents.

When his twelfth year came, he was to accompany his parents for the first time to the Passover feast in Jerusalem. After two weeks of preparation, they set off in the spring as part of a large caravan of pilgrims. Day after day as the men trudged along and the women rode on oxen and asses, they made their way down the Jordan valley; and he felt eager and at the same time strangely solemn.

They arrived in Jerusalem three days early. He was impressed with nothing as much as with the temple. Wandering about among the throngs of wide-eyed people, he thought the holy building the most meaningful place on earth. This was the spot, when it was nothing but a barren hill, where Abraham came to sacrifice his son Isaac. Here God had provided a substitute so that Isaac might live. Here Solomon had built the first temple, Zerubbabel the second, and Herod the third, which was as yet incomplete. Here sacrifices were brought that spoke to earth about the mysteries of heaven.

He watched the morning and evening sacrifices, and as blood flowed near the altar in the outer court his heart wrenched. He saw long lines of people waiting to bring sin offerings, ready to confess their offences on the heads of innocent animals. He saw priests entering the temple, symbol of God's presence, as carriers of the guilt of people.

'You look very serious,' his mother said at the end of the first day.

'It's the people's lack of understanding, Mother.' She looked at him questioningly. 'They're going through ceremonies without thinking what they mean. They imagine it must bring them favour with God.'

'But don't ceremonies do that?' she asked to his disappointment.

That evening his father wanted to speak to him. 'My son, the time has come for you to know something,' he said carefully. 'Your birth . . . well, it was not an ordinary one. An angel appeared to your mother and announced that you would be born.'

They did not know what to make of his silence.

'You see . . . Israel needs to be delivered from the Romans. We are being oppressed in our own country, ruled from Rome. Sooner or later, as everyone in Israel knows, God is going to send a deliverer.' He gave him a significant look. 'Like Gideon of old, he will deliver the people.'

He would say no more. They had been keeping this in their hearts all these years. Now, in the shadow of the temple, Jesus was discovering that an angel had spoken about him before his birth.

Passover day arrived, the fourteenth of Nisan, ordained by God to commemorate the great deliverance from Egyptian slavery. God had warned the Pharaoh of the final judgement on the Egyptians. The Hebrews sprinkled their door-posts with the blood of the slain lamb, and the angel of death passed over them to strike the first-born son of every Egyptian home, moving the king to set the slave nation free.

Jesus was among the worshippers, watching the white-robed priests, seeing the bleeding victim on the altar, bowing in prayer while the cloud of incense rose before God. Everything seemed bound up with his own life — the priests, the victim, the rising incense. New impulses were coming to life in him. He found himself avoiding people who wanted to chat. Here at the temple there was something of overwhelming importance that needed to be discovered. He prayed about it day by day, and also by night when others slept.

On the fifteen day of Nisan, a holy day, the Feast of

Unleavened Bread began, and the next day the wave sheaf of the first fruits was presented in the temple. Reflecting on all this, he went to a hall in the temple area where a rabbinical school was being held.

Here various rabbis sat with those who came to receive wisdom. There was an air of vast experience about them. They were grave custodians of the secrets of God, and everyone hung on their lips. They loved to argue, with one another as well as with their students. They relished talking in riddles, asking trick questions, leaving problems unsolved or 'solving' them with more than one answer — and often the answers contradicted one another, which to them was a special wisdom. They were also given to quoting endlessly from eminent rabbis of past ages, then arguing with gusto about the exact shade of meaning intended by the words of the sages.

A strong urge came to life in Jesus to witness to these learned men, and through them to those who had come to learn. How could he do so without presumption, without angering them? The rabbis were here to teach, not to learn — especially from a boy in his twelfth year. There was only one way: asking questions.

'Yes?' A rabbi lifted his heavy eyebrows at the boy's raised hand.

'Rabbi of mine, may I put a question?'

'Of course.'

'What is the meaning of the paschal lamb?'

'It signifies the deliverance of Israel from Egypt.'

'But why a lamb?'

'Well, why not a lamb?'

'I mean, why a sacrifice at all? Wasn't God's power the same, lamb or no lamb?'

'God commanded the lamb. That's all that matters. Of course God's power was the same, lamb or no lamb. But he commanded, for reasons of his own.'

'Are we not to understand what we are doing?' He spoke

so softly, eager to avoid a reaction of irritation or prejudice, that they had to ask him to repeat himself.

Laughing, they began to humour him. 'All right, let's hear the point of view of a boy of 12! What do you see in the lamb?'

'An innocent victim, rabbi of mine. Israel was not innocent. They did not deserve to be delivered.'

'What!' There was shock in the faces near him. 'Look here, boy — how can you say Israel did not deserve to be delivered? Don't you know that Israel are the descendants of righteous Abraham? Are you judging the Israel of God?'

'Even after their deliverance they murmured against God, and died in the desert because of their rebellion, my rabbi.'

'Aha, not bad for a boy. I was just testing your knowledge. So Israel was not innocent. And the lamb?'

'The lamb represented innocence. The innocence that Israel needed to be worthy of deliverance.'

The man winked slyly. 'A lamb can never be anything but innocent. It is a dumb creature, incapable of sin. So how could there be merit in its innocence?'

'Is it possible, my rabbi, that the lamb did not stand for its own innocence, but for the righteousness of God?'

There was another shock wave. All over the hall they started debating among themselves. After some minutes another rabbi silenced them.

'The boy is right. Only God could justify unjust Israel. And the only righteousness he could draw upon to cover them as with a garment was his own righteousness. But, boy, why a lamb, as you asked in the beginning? Why not just a word, a pronouncement by God? Surely no lamb needed to enter the picture?'

'Was the lamb needed, my rabbi, not only for its innocence but also for its blood?'

'Its blood?'

'In the book of Leviticus it is written, "The life of the

body is in the blood. It is the blood that atones for the guilt of the soul." '

They began to crowd around him.

'Ah,' said a student sentimentally. 'The magic properties of blood. The mystical qualities of blood are pleasing to our God.'

Jesus could not remain silent on this point. 'May I quote from the prophet Isaiah? " 'Why do you bring a host of sacrifices to me?' says the Lord. 'I take no delight in the blood of bulls or lambs or goats.' " Isn't it better to think of the blood as symbolizing the life, which is what counts?'

Day by day this kind of thing happened. He would listen in silence for a long time, then humbly ask questions in an effort to lead others' minds to the heart of God's plan to save people. He set himself to be self-effacing, yet he had a witness that he simply had to bring. As one seeking wisdom — which he was doing day and night — he raised the question of Abraham, ready to sacrifice Isaac on this hill when God provided an innocent life to take the boy's place. On another day, one of the days of the Feast of Unleavened Bread following Passover, he asked why God said through the prophet Isaiah that he hated the Hebrews' feasts. It was more than an hour before all present were led to admit, although with reluctance on the part of the rabbis, that no ritual has any value unless the believer places his life in harmony with God and the divine will. Wasn't ritual-and-ceremony worse than useless, the boy asked, wasn't it in fact dangerous when we otherwise live our lives apart from God — because going through the motions of religion gave us a false sense of security?

Between discussions he kept up his study of the Scriptures and prayerfully meditated on the meaning of the temple and its services. The subject of the promised Messiah was often in his mind. Gleams of light were breaking through to his mind; the nagging mystery was beginning to open to him.

At the same time he felt painfully burdened to arrest his dear people in their thoughtless performance of ceremonies. They had to be taught to look beyond outward things to the heart of the matter, the true meaning. The school at the temple offered him the best chance to be heard.

One day while he was at the temple his parents and their friends decided to end their stay. By the middle of the day they had packed and left. That evening Jesus discovered what had happened, and agonized over whether to hurry after them or keep the appointment he had with some young seekers for truth at the temple the next day. He could not understand why his dear parents had left without letting him know — possibly they had been rushed by friends.

In his quandary he spent much of the night in prayer, on the site where his family had camped. In the middle of the night heaven came very close, and he saw that his heavenly Father required his first loyalty: that he needed to witness for God in the temple. With this, his problem vanished, and he slept on the ground. Early the next morning, not having eaten since he shared his lunch with a friend the previous afternoon, he was back at the temple, remaining there all day and speaking about God in the school and outside.

That evening he went back to the campsite, where he could easily be found if his parents were looking for him. All night no one came. Little did he know that his parents had discovered his absence the previous evening, were now back at Jerusalem but on another campsite, and had spent half the day hunting for him wherever they saw groups of children at play or lounging about on street corners.

The next morning, still not having eaten since two days previously, he was back with the doctors of sacred law. Today their topic was the promised Messiah — a subject that stirred deep emotions in the boy.

'Israel needs the Messiah,' one rabbi was saying by mid-morning. 'We are being ground under the heel of Rome.

When we were slaves in the pestilential country of Egypt, God sent Moses to deliver us. Before Moses died, God said to him, "I will raise up a prophet for them from among their people, one like yourself." Today, my brothers, we need this deliverer. In a sense we are worse off than in Egypt. In an alien country it is not unnatural to lack freedom. But we are in our own country. We are in the Promised Land! And in this land, God's land, Roman soldiers dominate us and our taxes flow to Rome — to pagan Rome! Brothers, if ever Israel needed the promised deliverer it is now!'

They erupted in a snarling hatred of the Romans. Jesus thought sadly: If a man of strong personality appeared now and proclaimed himself the Messiah, they would embrace him, follow him to the death. *Provided* he declared war on the Romans.

'What will the Messiah do when he comes, my rabbi?' he asked.

The teacher welcomed the question. 'He will remind us that we were destined to be the head of the nations, not the tail. That the wealth of the nations must flow to us, not our taxes to them. That all nations are to call us blessed. And how will these things come about, the Messiah will challenge us, while we put our neck under the heel of Rome, a pagan nation? He will call us to rise! We will throw off the yoke! He will be our deliverer from alien bondage!' His cheeks trembled, his voice shook, his fist stabbed the air and his eyes struck sparks from his audience.

'Would he be successful in his mission, my rabbi?'

He fixed the boy with a fiery glance. 'Of course! What a question! It is the promise of the Almighty! Why? Because we are the seed of Abraham! No one can stand against the promised Servant of heaven! He will vanquish all our enemies. Could Egypt defeat Moses? Could the Midianite armies defeat Gideon and his three hundred? Our enemies will be driven into the sea! All Gentiles will come and worship at our feet!'

'Will this victory last, my rabbi?'

'It will last! We will never taste weakness or defeat again — never! We will sit under our fig trees and our vines, never again to fight and struggle. Our deliverer will be our King!'

'Then the deliverer will have to be very exalted, very great, his fame and praise on everyone's lips.'

'Exactly! Without knowing it, you have just quoted the prophet Isaiah. God's promised Servant will prosper, everything will go his way, all the world will extol his greatness!'

'Then why, my rabbi, does Isaiah go on to say that his appearance will be marred more than that of any other man, that he will be despised and rejected?'

It was a boy's soft piping voice, but the effect was electric. A profound silence held them while the teacher stared heavenward. Eventually another theologian cleared his throat and spoke up.

'Yes, that passage by the prophet Isaiah does pertain to the promised deliverer, as all our rabbinical wisdom to this moment asserts . . . '

'Then you've got a problem!' another interjected. 'Because Isaiah says the promised one is rejected, taken to the slaughter, vanquished!'

The first teacher stopped gazing heavenward for help, and looked at Jesus. 'So you see, boy, you've got a problem.' He picked at his long beard. 'What does your little mind make of the problem?' He pulled the corners of his mouth down, and there were chuckles everywhere.

'My rabbi, Isaiah says the promised one is cut off from among the living and makes his grave with those considered wicked. Later he says he prolongs his days, everything prospers in his hand, he is great and strong.'

'How can the two go together?'

'Must they go together, my rabbi?'

'You mean . . . ?'

'Why not two different times? First, he comes as a lamb. Later, as a King?'

'But then . . . who is to deliver us from the Romans?'

'Isn't there perhaps something worse to be delivered from?'

'Never! Nothing!'

They argued among themselves, so vehemently that it sounded like a brawl. They wanted a deliverer-king now, not later. They wanted liberation — not of soul, but of body.

Someone asked if Isaiah's words could be applied to Israel's future, not to the Deliverer-Servant. He was silenced with arguments that this was unacceptable. Israel was to be delivered, not consigned to the grave; and Israel would *never* be dumb as a lamb before the shearers — *never!* Nor would Israel ever take upon itself the sins of others — never.

And because men must always try to move God's mountainous word, using the lever of man's devious reasoning and venerable traditions, they appealed to the rabbis — but found that tradition up to now, as expounded by famous teachers, also supported the Messianic interpretation of Isaiah's words.

A kindly rabbi took Jesus by the shoulder. 'You must come and study under us, my boy,' he smiled. 'You've got a good potential. You could become a famous rabbi, a Shammai or a Hillel, if you studied in our schools.'

He glanced around and lowered his voice. 'You think the Messiah will first be a child before he's a man?'

'Didn't Moses say he would be just like Moses himself, my teacher? And wasn't Moses a child before he became a man?'

'True, true. But . . . will he really die? Die, as I must die and you must die?'

'Isn't the sin-offering animal put to death, my preacher? And if an animal's life cannot atone for men's sins, must a higher life not pay the price?'

He forgot to hide his surprise, then patted the boy's

shoulder. 'Remember, you must come and study in our school. You could become famous!' he said, turning away.

Mary was suddenly there, gripping his arm. 'My son!' she exclaimed, her voice aggrieved. 'Why did you do this to us! Your father and I have been looking for you all over Jerusalem!'

All over Jerusalem? Two nights ago, as he prayed on that vacant campsite, the Holy Spirit gave him an insight into the heavenly announcement that preceded his coming to this planet. With such memories of things they had lived through, why hadn't Joseph and Mary come straight to the only logical place, the temple?

'Why did you look elsewhere, Mother? Didn't you know I would be nowhere but in my Father's house?' he asked gently, pointing heavenward on the word 'Father'.

He was doing the work for which he had come into this world. They had neglected their work by losing sight of the One whom heaven had entrusted to their care. So far had they forgotten heaven's messages surrounding his birth, that they had searched for him a whole day without thinking of the temple. And now, how typical of human nature that they should be reproving him instead of themselves.

'Your Father's house?' his mother asked, drawing him close and lowering her head to speak in his ear.

A man had thrown an arm over Joseph's shoulder and they were chatting. Jesus knew he would still respectfully call Joseph his father, in spite of what the Spirit had revealed to him here in Jerusalem.

'Mother . . . didn't the angel say to you that the child must be called Jesus, and that he would be called the Son of the Most High?'

'I — I never told you!' she exclaimed.

'I have known since two nights ago.'

In a society whose demands were in constant collision with the requirements of God, Jesus lived till he was thirty. He walked alone. He was familiar with poverty, self-denial and privation. He knew no idle moments, no aimless hours — a blessing of inestimable value. There was constant peer pressure on him to join in lighthearted worldliness. He knew there would be pleasure and applause if he said yes, mockery and criticism if he said no. There were appeals to appetite, pride, popularity. There was constant pressure in his home and from the religious leaders to conform to well-meant traditions that defeated God's plan with the human soul. His help was from the Lord, and his main protection the Scriptures.

He learned a trade, developed muscles, calloused hands, and a cheerful, positive and energetic spirit. In the bitterness of opposition he learned the hard lesson of silence and patient endurance. He did his best to show the love of God for every human being — even towards dumb creatures. At the same time he tried to show the hatred of God for sin. Called coward, fanatic, rebel, he refused to regard any provocation as an excuse for sin — not even the sin of impatience. He would not retaliate, because he lived in the light of God's presence. When remonstrated with by those he specially loved, he made allowance for the fact that they did not understand his mission. His particular friends were little children, 'who come to me', he told himself, 'only for love and understanding and never as agents of temptation'. All his friends married and drifted into worlds of their own. This would never be for him, he knew, because the way had to be opened for men and women of all nations who were looking for escape from the second death. Not only sordid Nazareth, but the whole world needed the way, the truth, and the life.

Later, Jesus was to say about John the Baptist that he was a burning and shining light, and that no man ever born of woman had been more highly regarded by heaven.

Isaiah had foretold 'the voice of him that cries in the wilderness, "Prepare the way of the Lord, make a straight highway in the desert for our God . . . . The glory of the Lord shall be revealed, and all people shall see it." ' To this the prophet Malachi had added God's promise, 'I will send my messenger and he shall prepare the way before me, and the Lord whom you expected shall suddenly come to his temple.'

Just a few hundred years later, John was the first fulfilment of these prophecies. He was to introduce the Promised One to the world. No other prophet, not even the redoubtable Elijah, had received so great a privilege.

It was decided in heaven that the Creator's power must be seen not only in John's life but also in his birth, to make clear man's inadequacy and God's power. An elderly couple, well past the reproductive time of life — and she barren and childless all her life — were selected for the privilege by reason of their character: 'both righteous before God.' He had an additional qualification — for many years he had been praying for the coming of the Messiah.

One day while it was his turn to minister at the temple, the great angel of the Lord, Gabriel, appeared to him and said, 'Don't be afraid, Zacharias. Your prayer has been heard.

'Your wife Elizabeth will bear you a son whom you must call John. His birth will bring you and many others happiness. In God's sight he will be great, never touching wine or strong drink. The Holy Spirit will be fully active in him. He will turn many of the children of Israel to the Lord their God. He will go before the Lord in the spirit and power of Elijah . . . to make ready a people prepared for the Lord.'

Five hundred years earlier this selfsame Gabriel had told the prophet Daniel about Messiah the Prince who would come and be 'cut off', though not on his own account. For years Zacharias had been pondering this prophecy, probing its details, and praying for the coming of the Promised One. Yet now, when told that he was to have a miraculously conceived son who would announce to the world that the Messiah had come, when assured that more than his fondest hopes were about to be realized . . . his faith faltered.

'But . . . by what shall I know this? We're much too old, my wife and I . . . '

How sad that the sign of the glorious angel himself was not enough for him. He was granted a further sign — the unwelcome one of dumbness, until John should be born.

Nine months later, back at his home in the Judean hills, Zacharias's dumbness vanished as he named the baby — not 'Zacharias' as all the rest of the family insisted, but 'John' as Gabriel had instructed him.

A greater miracle than his birth was John's quality of soul. He could have set his free will against God's ideals for him. Instead, as child and man, he decided for God. He learned how to open his heart to his Creator in prayer, was taught how to read and write, from scrolls of the sacred Scriptures which his priest-father owned, and became an avid student of God's Word.

Ordinarily, he would have been educated for the priesthood. But the training of the rabbinical schools would subtly have unfitted him for the greatest work ever committed to a man. He needed a tuition which only God could give.

In the desert he found this, with the Scriptures in his hand and the lessons of nature and providential guidance before him. Like his Lord, he would not be the product of the schools of his day. These were the decisive years of his life — the years of his youth. His life-style was simple in the extreme, often hard, and from it he learned to discipline himself in mind and body. Every day he reminded himself of his mission in life, as he had learned the details from his parents; and every day he received greater light in prayer, meditation and a study of the Word.

Although based in the wilderness, he was a keen observer of the passing human scene. The life of a hermit would have unbalanced him, unfitting him for his work; so from time to time he set forth to mingle with men and gain an insight into the workings of their minds. During these brief excursions he was careful not to linger amid influences that could lower the moral tone of his life. Even so, he was not free from temptations. There were forces determined to bring him to a fall. In the power of the Holy Spirit he was unusually alert to every danger, developing strength and decisiveness with every moral victory.

The hour struck when heaven gave him his marching orders. His public career was going to be brief — a mere two years. He had no inkling of this, yet plunged into his preaching with the vigour and power of extreme urgency.

The nation was in a state of ferment. The Roman governors ruled with an iron hand. Often dealing unfairly with the Hebrews, they got their blood up further by foisting heathen symbols and customs on them. To add to the strain, there was a pervasive excitement springing from a conviction that the Messiah was soon to come.

In this tense climate a 30-year-old man began to attract huge audiences to the wilderness. Dressed in the camel's hair robe of a prophet, John had a message arrestingly simple: *'Repent! The kingdom of God is at hand!'* It moved the people as nothing ever had. In the spirit and power of an Elijah of old he denounced the national corruption and rebuked the sins of the people. Multitudes flocked to him: rabbis and soldiers, peasants and men of wealth and influence.

'Confess your sins to God and get ready to meet the Deliverer!' John proclaimed. As he named their sins one by one, many a heart quailed before his spiritual power. Without purification, he said, no one could be part of the

Messiah's kingdom. Instructed by the Holy Spirit, he baptized many in the Jordan River as a symbol of cleansing.

Some came with false motives. John, impressed by the Spirit, denounced their shallowness. 'Don't think your descent from Abraham will do you any good! God could change these stones into children of Abraham. Bear fruit to show that your lives are changed! Then come and I will baptize you.'

The changed character — that was the key to the Messiah's kingdom. The qualities of God's character — kindness, honesty, a caring spirit, justice, mercy, love and loyalty — must be seen in them. They must be in harmony with God's law. The heart and life would determine their standing with God.

IN THE JORDAN 6

In my devotions one morning while it was still dark, I had heard the voice of God calling me to leave my secular duties to others. Later that morning a man came to the carpenter's shop that had been Joseph's, and when he spoke about the prophet in the wilderness and his startling message, I knew what to do and took leave of Mary, my tearful mother.

I joined the crowds that followed John. As I listened from a distance to John's dynamic sermons, full of Scripture and metaphors from nature, I felt the same inner stirrings as when studying the temple services in Jerusalem eighteen years earlier. I watched the people's faces. They were awed, as in the presence of an Elijah descended from heaven.

'I baptize you in water as testimony to your repentance,' was John's ever-recurring refrain. 'But the One who comes after me is mightier than I. I am not fit to take off his sandals. He will baptize you with the Holy Spirit and with fire!'

How all you people would pluck off your sandals, I

mused, if you knew that the ground on which you are standing is the holy ground of the burning bush.

John and I were cousins, but we had never had any contact with each other. I had been confined to Nazareth; he had lived his life in the wilds of Judea. Now the time had come for us to meet.

One morning, waiting for God's instructions under the stars, I received the enlightenment of the Holy Spirit. It had been revealed to John that the Messiah would ask him for baptism, I saw. A sign would be given him that this was indeed the Christ, the Anointed. John's mission would then reach its climax when he identified and introduced the Promised One to history.

I waited that morning, anonymous in the crowd, jostled by priests and scribes, artisans and fishermen. These people had left their means of livelihood and come long distances, some five days on foot, to hear the prophet of God. All hung on John's words. In his coarse garb and leather belt, hair and beard full but not unkempt, he was a rugged, arresting figure. His voice was powerful, with an unusual carrying quality. With penetrating eyes and dynamic gestures, he spoke directly and simply.

He made his daily call for repentance. People, some refined and others rough-looking, pressed forward into the clearing. Ignoring the rest of us, he urged them to hold nothing back from God, to rely on divine power to live the new life.

'The kingdom of heaven is at hand! Now is the time to make sure that you are true citizens of it!'

He prayed over them, turned and waded waist-deep into the Jordan. One at a time they followed him and he immersed them in the name of God.

After ten minutes he reached the last candidate for baptism, a pock-marked man of about forty. I made my way past some people and into the river. When John raised the man to his feet, I was standing at his elbow.

He looked at me and I at him. Two strangers — yet the same divine Spirit ruled his life as directed mine. A wonderful flow of soul took place between us. It was a sublime moment.

'You must baptize me, Yochanan,' I said.

He stood, head slightly to one side, as though listening to retreating echoes of my voice.

'You?' he asked softly. 'You?'

How my heart glowed for him. A man of God, true and stalwart. He was the first person I had met in thirty years who was a Scripture-saturated, totally dedicated servant of God.

'*No!*' he exclaimed. 'How can I? I'm a sinner. You should baptize me! And you come to me . . . for baptism?'

I nodded. Yes, John, not as a repentant sinner but as part of my identification with sinners, with mankind. To set an example. To put the stamp of Christ on your baptism.

'At this moment, Yochanan, this is what must be done. It is what God requires.'

I felt the trembling of his hands. His voice shook in prayer. He lowered me backwards, immersed and raised me.

The crowd opened as I left the water and knelt in prayer, face upturned. From here on the battle would be fought to the death. I would walk alone, not understood by anyone, not by my mother, not even by John the Baptist. While my heart ached for peace, I must walk in strife. While I yearned for purity, the clamour of sin would be all about me, a torment to my spirit. I would be rejected, slandered, abused; my mission would be misunderstood, my Father misrepresented.

As I poured out my soul for strength to go through with it all, and pleaded with tears for reassurance that God would accept humanity in the person of his Son, an intense beam of light broke through the blue of the sky. All about me was light, above me a pure dancing radiance like a fluttering dove. The voice echoed down the path of light: 'This is my Son, the Beloved, in whom I take delight.'

I rise and move on, hearing John's choked voice behind me. 'There he is, the Lamb of God! He is the one who takes away the sin of the world!' John has received his sign from heaven; but he still does not understand the full import of his own words.

NEAR DEATH 7

The Holy Spirit had also directed me that morning to go up into the arid wastes after baptism. Obediently, I gathered up my only luggage — my precious bundle of Scripture scrolls — and started off alone. I had need to be alone, to think of what lay ahead and brace myself for the battle.

After the first day of prayer and study of the Scriptures, I heaped up a little pile of sand for a pillow, spread part of my robe over it and lay down near an overhang yielding slow drops of water.

Almost at once the Holy Spirit opened my mind to an arresting sight. I saw the centre of the universe, the radiant Sanctuary of God, and innumerable angels. An imposing leader of angels rebelled against the authority of the Most High. There was what seemed to be a war in heaven, and the rebel and his host of angel followers were overcome. As I watched, the rebel fell like lightning from the heavens to an outlying planet that was, relatively speaking, a mere grain of sand in the universe of God, and here he and his supporters continued the war.

The next morning I read in my copy of Isaiah's seven-hundred-year-old book, 'How are you fallen from heaven, O day star, son of the morning!' He had vaunted himself to equality with God: 'You thought to yourself, "I will ascend into heaven, I will exalt my throne above the stars of God, all creatures will gather before me as I sit on high, exalted above all like the Most High".'

On the surface, this was the king of Babylon; by the light of the Spirit I saw that this was more saliently the Enemy, Satan, the bright one who fell into rebellion.

Under a different figure God, speaking through the prophet Ezekiel, said of this same leader of rebellion, 'You are the anointed angel of great privilege. I appointed you. You were in God's presence . . . You were perfect in everything from the day you were created till you sinned . . . You were in Eden, the garden of God . . . I will cast you to the ground.'

For hours on end I contemplated these and other clues to the created being who thought he could vanquish the Almighty and now called himself the ruler of Planet Earth. He had declared war on me the day I was born, I knew. I would have to contend with him for the rest of my life. He had heard the words from heaven after my baptism, 'This is my Son, the Beloved.' He had no further uncertainty as to my true identity.

On the second day, fasting and much of the time in prayer, I became aware of temptations. John was just a puny figure preaching in the wilds — how could such a man's work effectively prepare the way for the Messiah? Here was I, surrounded by boulders and sand, flying insects and a fierce heat haze, incongruously poised on the brink of a cosmic battle. Was it worth what it would cost me in suffering and danger? How inviting the rude house and workshop of Nazareth looked from here! I refused to nurse these thoughts, but as I pushed them away other whispers assailed me and had to be repulsed. Prayer and fasting, fasting and prayer — this battle would have to be fought to the finish.

The physical distress that came with weeks of fasting was pushed to the background of consciousness. My mind did not dwell on hunger, on food, but on God. I felt more and more shut in with my Father, borne up by a tenderness beyond words, my soul nourished with the bread of life. With all my heart I sought strength and grace to meet the foe, help the tempted, and fulfil my saving mission.

On the fortieth day the sublime vision of God's presence passed away, and like a flood the hunger and weakness engulfed me. I was mere skin and bone, worn and haggard with the spiritual struggle. The craving for food was a cry from every cell in my body. I had no strength to reach civilization to obtain food. This test was necessary. From Adam and Eve on, it was in appetite and passion that nearly all humans lost their way. As man's representative I had to exercise a self-control stronger than hunger and death.

The next morning found me holding onto an outcrop of rock, trembling, unsteady. Would my Father not send me help? As my mind panted this plea, I became aware of a brightness nearby, a brightness that became an angel.

'Greetings from heaven!' he said pleasantly. I could only stare. He raised a hand. 'It is enough. Your fast has been accepted in heaven. When Abraham raised his knife obediently to slay his son Isaac, God stopped him by the voice of an angel. Just so your willing obedience has been accepted, and I have been sent to deliver you from death. In God's name, your fast may now be broken. Do you see those stones at your feet, so very like loaves of bread? If you are the Son of God, command that they become bread!'

I needed bread desperately. Might my Father send an angel to intervene mercifully? Yes, it fully accorded with his love. Had I the power to give such a command? Yes.

But there were two false notes here. I was being asked to work a miracle on my own behalf. *My own behalf!* To exercise divine power for my own benefit is *not* why I came to this planet; nor does such action harmonize with the spirit of heaven.

Secondly — that 'if'. 'If' you are the Son of God. This implied unbelief. Had not the Father said, 'This is my Son'?

I made no move to take up the angel's challenge. He waited, then in a voice full of sympathy said, 'You are exhausted. This has dulled your brain. But just speak the word, and eat.' He pointed to the stones.

I did not respond. 'Listen,' he said earnestly. 'We in heaven know, and you know, that one of heaven's most powerful angels was banished to this planet. Can you imagine him — his ravaged appearance, emaciated, tottering about? Forsaken by God, an outcast, a gaunt scarecrow? Do I need to point out that this is a picture that exactly fits you? The question is inescapable: Are you that fallen angel? There is one test. Turn these stones into bread. Use your creative power to prove you are not the fallen angel!'

I kept my soul uplifted in prayer. *Never* parley with temptation, I told myself.

'Man shall not live by bread alone,' I said, quoting from Deuteronomy, 'but by every word God utters.' God's will was my food. I'd rather starve to death than possibly violate his will.

'Well done,' said the angel after a momentary pause. 'Now, come with me.'

Close to collapse as I was, I found that the angel and I were moving effortlessly and swiftly through the air.

Jerusalem came into view. Streaking down, we were suddenly standing on a high point of the temple complex. For my humanity it was a breath-taking experience, meant to overwhelm me with an impression of divine power.

'The stones-to-bread idea was a test of your loyalty,' he said. 'But the time has come for you to prove your faith in God and his Scriptures. Scripture says in a certain Psalm, "He will put his angels in charge of you. They will put their arms under you to make sure you do not so much as strike your foot against a stone." If you are the Son of God, prove your faith in God's Word by throwing yourself down!'

But Psalm ninety-one, I thought to myself, starts with the words, 'He who dwells in the secret places of the Most

High will remain under the protection of the Almighty.' And the 'secret place' is God's will. What you're asking me to do is not God's will. Your 'if' puts God's testimony in doubt.

I stared at the angel. How innocent his face, how bright his presence! Yet he was the great enemy. He was quoting Scripture, but deceptively.

'Scripture says, "You are not to put the Lord your God to the test",' I answered, quoting from Deuteronomy.

But for a crease that appeared between those clear eyes, nothing changed in the angel's face. 'Come!' he said.

We were moving again, clouds below us, then descending till we stood on a mountain.

'I'll make you an offer,' the angel said quietly. 'But first, look at this.'

Before us, as in a mirage, appeared a city, its spired temples and marble palaces gleaming in the sun. More cities flashed into existence, so real I felt I could join the crowds thronging their streets. The cities made way for lush fields, verdant valleys, farm paradises. After my forty days of desolate landscape it was a display of awesome beauty.

'All this belongs to me,' my tempter said. 'I know who you are and you know who I am. The world belongs to me. Its people follow my ideas. I'm prepared to hand it all over to you, here and now! On one condition. Go down on your knees to me. Then everything on this planet is yours!'

My mind went to the nation among whom I had chosen to be born. I loved them, but they would reject me. How gladly they would embrace me as their Messiah if I offered them what the enemy was offering me — worldly glory!

Men would always sell me for the world. Was it really worthwhile going ahead with the plan for saving men, in view of all the suffering and slander I'd have to face?

'Be off, Satan! Scripture says, "You shall worship the Lord your God and serve only him." '

I uttered the command in the power of the Father. Satan

drew back trembling, and as impotent rage began to over-whelm him he disappeared.

Like a dying man I sank to the rocky ledge, and became aware of angels from my Father. They served me, revived me with food and reassurances that all heaven rejoiced in my victory, and helped me down off the mountain.

THE LAMB

8

John's desert audience had grown even vaster, covering the craggy terrain like ants. Strangely, their excitement was marked by restraint, as though they were solemnized by what they had heard.

As I moved in among them some stared. In my emaciated state I must have looked very unprepossessing. None recognized me from my baptism forty-two days ago. In spite of all the outward differences among them, I thought, there were just two classes here: those who had opened their hearts to John's message, and those who had not.

I became aware of an important-looking man who seemed intent on everything John said. Our paths would cross, I knew.

Just then a richly robed group appeared. They saw the important man, hesitated, went over and deferentially exchanged a few words with him. Then they turned towards John.

It soon became apparent that they were a deputation of religious leaders sent by the Sanhedrin in Jerusalem to estab-lish John's credentials. As overseer of religion to the nation, the Sanhedrin obviously felt the need to authorize or disap--prove the work of this influential new preacher.

'Who are you?' I heard the group's leader demand of John.

John looked them over. He knew what was in their minds. Did he claim to be the Messiah? Who but the

Messiah could so excite the whole nation with the hope of national deliverance?

'I am not the Christ,' John said.

'Well, who are you then? Elijah?'

Since they took Malachi's prophecy about the return of Elijah literally instead of figuratively, John could only shake his head. He was not Elijah in person. 'I am not,' he said.

'Are you that prophet?' Now they were thinking of Moses.

'No.'

'Identify yourself. We must give an answer to those who sent us. What do you call yourself?'

'I am the voice of one crying in the wilderness, "Make straight the way of the Lord", according to the prophet Isaiah.'

This was his mission exactly. As workmen in ancient times went before the royal chariot to level the way by hacking away at humps and filling up holes, so John's preaching must abase pride and exalt humility. By calling men to repentance he was preparing their hearts to accept the Messiah.

'Then who gave you authority to baptize, if you're not the promised Christ, nor Elijah, nor that prophet?'

At that moment John saw me. He stared so fixedly that the people between us began to look over their shoulders. In spite of the change in my appearance, John recognized me. His face turned ecstatic and he pointed with both arms extended.

'I baptize in water, but there is one among you over there whom you don't know! One who takes over from me, whose sandals I'm not worthy to undo!'

The Sanhedrin's men had their answer. The Messiah was among them; let them go and study the Messianic Scriptures and see what message they really contained.

No one followed me as I left.

The next day John saw me again. At once his face was

transformed. Pointing, he cried, 'There he is, the Lamb of God who takes away the sin of the world! The one I pointed out as being after me, yet before me!'

They jostled and strained to see the one about whom the august Sanhedrin had inquired, the one greater than John the Baptist. Alas, all they saw was a simple human like themselves, clad in the humble garments of the poor and looking as though he had not eaten in a long time.

'I tell you, before I was born, he already was! I never met him, but the only reason why I came preaching and baptizing in water was to introduce him to Israel!'

My eye fell on Nathanael, one of John's most devoted disciples. He was deeply disappointed. He was staring at poverty, at an emaciated frame. The Messiah? How could it be?

John seemed to sense that no one was convinced. What faith it must have cost him to continue, 'I saw the Spirit coming down from heaven like a dove and resting upon him! I had never met him, but he who sent me to baptize in water told me, "When you see the Spirit descending on someone and resting upon him, you will know that this is he who is to baptize with the Holy Spirit." With my own eyes I saw it! I have given my word on it! This is the Son of God!'

His voice thrilled with certainty and joy, and I quietly thanked my Father for a man like the Baptizer. So powerful was his faith that no one could shrug off his words. Many stared at me, intrigued and perplexed, as I made my way through the crowd and along a footpath, trying to draw them to follow me. To my disappointment no one hurried after me with questions, and I knew I would have to give John's disciples yet another opportunity.

This came the next day. John, flanked by two disciples on a rise, saw me at once as I skirted the crowd. 'There is the Lamb of God!' he said to those near him.

Not understanding, but alive to John's testimony, the two disciples pushed through the crowd and followed me.

One was Andrew and the other John, namesake of the Baptist. It lifted my spirits to know that they were behind me. John had worked so hard for more than half a year to bring this about. They were so slow to respond, already two days behind heaven's guidance. But there they were now, the unforced very precious first fruits.

Should I turn and say to them, 'Congratulations! You've made the right decision'? No. That would put subtle pressure on them to throw in their lot with me. They must be given every chance to turn back.

Turning, I asked, 'What are you looking for?'

They could have said, 'Are you really the Messiah?' as the men from the Sanhedrin would have done. But they didn't. 'Rabbi,' they said respectfully, 'where are you staying?'

I was thrilled. Deep men these; men of the right spirit.

'Come and see,' I said.

Our footpath followed the course of the Jordan and passed a rude abandoned fisherman's shack. Its door was missing, the roof — probably of skins sewn together — was gone and much of its timber was crumbling. I stopped and smiled. 'This is my home.' It would put their faith to a further test. I had come across it three days ago and thought it a welcome haven after sleeping in the open.

It shocked them, but we stepped inside and sat on the floor next to the spread of hay which was my bed. There were about two hours of sunlight left. We talked, and soon they had forgotten all about their surroundings as I led them along the royal highway of the Scriptures. Their faces, as God's truth of incalculable value opened to their minds, were the most cheering sight I had seen since those precious moments after my baptism when the Father beamed his own glory from heaven.

As the sun began to set Andrew said, 'Master, I must go! I must find my brother Simon and tell him I've found the Messiah!'

'I am spending the night here,' I said. He hurried off and John, intense and thoughtful by nature, was ready with more questions.

An hour later Andrew was back, out of breath. 'This is Simon, Master! I told him we'd found the Messiah, and he came at once.'

I looked at the strongly-built man of about twenty-six. He had been deeply impressed with John and his wilderness sermons. A complex man — impulsive, aggressive, sympathetic, proud, ambitious, self-confident.

'You are Simon the son of John,' I told him. 'You will be known as Stone.' Or, as this name would be shaped by the universal influence of the Greek language, 'Peter'.

We sat in the light of the full moon, talking far into the night.

Before break of day as I was praying, my mind was led to Nathanael, true-hearted disciple of John. I had never spoken to him, but needed him. At John's exclamation, 'There is the Lamb of God!' he had looked at me keenly, bitterly disappointed at what he saw. My emaciated appearance and obvious poverty put him in a quandary. How could I be the Christ . . . yet how could John's testimony be unreliable?

From my place of prayer, I saw him going to a quiet place to think things through and restudy the Messianic prophecies. Eventually, screened by the branches of the fig tree under which he sat, he prayed that if the one pointed out by John really was the Christ it might be brought forcibly home to him. As he ended his prayer a friend found him in his hiding place and told him about me.

An hour later, with this glimpse into events about to take place fresh before me, I was ready for the five days' hike to Galilee. I made a detour away from the river and met six men on their way to John in the wilderness. All six had been with John when he pointed me out. One of them was

Nathanael's friend, about to play such a key role in influencing Nathanael.

'Your name is Philip,' I said. 'Follow me.'

I strode on, and almost at once he was with me, having left his friends behind. After a few moments I said, 'Before we go any further, is there anything you feel you must do?'

'I have a special friend, Master,' he began hesitantly.

'I'll wait for you at the rock of Adad,' I said, and with a look of surprise he hurried off. I had been shown that his as yet trembling faith would cause him to say to Nathanael that I was the son of Joseph, instead of stressing that I was the Son of God. Nathanael would find this confusing, but at Philip's mention of my being from Nazareth he would throw up his arms and exclaim, 'Can anything good come from Nazareth?'

Soon I saw the two approaching, Philip eager, Nathanael plodding. When they were close I said to Nathanael, 'Here is an Israelite in more than name! There is nothing false in him.'

This brought him up short. 'But — how do you come to know me?'

'I saw you under the fig tree before Philip found you there.'

His reservations crumbled before the onrush of faith. 'Rabbi, you *are* the Son of God! You *are* the King of Israel!' What an example to Philip!

'Do you believe just because I told you I saw you under the fig tree? You will see greater proofs than this.' He would see the genuinely sick genuinely healed, the dead raised to life, and most remarkably the worldly soul changed into the heavenly. All this would be done by the ministry of angels from God, the Messiah providing the link between the needs of humans and the fullness of heaven. Coupling these thoughts with the opening of the heavens above me after my baptism, I said, 'I assure you, you will see heaven wide open and God's angels ascending and descending upon the Son of Man.'

CANA

9

Back at Nazareth after a two months' absence, I found that my mother had gone to nearby Cana for a wedding. My friends and I at once set out for that little village. I knew how deeply stirred my mother had been by the reports she heard of John's wilderness messages. John's work confirmed her treasured memories of my supernatural birth. Doubts had crept in at times, and disappointment when I seemed too nonconformist as far as national religious ideas and customs were concerned. Now she must have heard of my baptism, followed by the glory beamed from heaven.

We met at our relatives' home in Cana, Mother looking relieved and happy. Yet there was concern in the way her eyes followed me. I had not yet fully recovered from the forty days in the wilderness. She probably also saw something else in my face that she couldn't understand. The group of young men who followed me and called me master confirmed that something mysterious had happened to me.

On the morning of the wedding she talked to John, my disciple, privately. He told her all he knew and said, 'He is the one about whom Moses and the prophets wrote.'

What a happy occasion a wedding can be! As I watched the young couple linking their lives, I rejoiced with them. They were so innocent, so loving. I congratulated them warmly, smiling into their bright eyes, and urged them to make their union God-centred.

The festivities that followed were marked by a happiness that was never marred by raucous folly. I felt at home, enjoying the smiles and good cheer.

Watching my mother I realized that she was hoping I'd

prove to the guests that I was the Christ. A very human yearning, springing partly from maternal pride; but this was not the pre-planned time for the Messiah to come in the glory of his kingdom.

She was almost glad when the wine gave out. Full of eager expectancy, she hurried to where I stood with my disciples and said, 'They've no wine left!'

She was trying to force my hand, eager that I prove myself to the guests with a miracle.

Using the respectful and formal mode of address, I said, 'O woman, why should that concern you or me?'

She remained concerned, not only over this minor matter but that I should reveal myself as the Messiah. To honour her trust in me, and more importantly to reinforce the faith of my disciples against the great temptations that lay before them, I'd do something about the wine; but I'd make no Messianic claims now. 'My hour has not yet come,' I explained.

Only half understanding, but encouraged by my expression, she said to the servants as she left the room, 'Do whatever he tells you to do.'

With the disciples watching, I told the servants, 'Go and draw water and fill those six stone jars.'

While they struggled with the heavy jars, I thought of Joseph in an Egyptian prison because of Potiphar's wife, and Pharaoh's wine steward telling him how he prepared wine by squeezing the grapes in his master's presence into the cup and handing it to the king. That was what I would have preferred to do now — set my disciples to pressing some grapes for the guests. But the matter was too urgent. I'd provide wine, new and fresh, that would not set men to mocking and raging, as Solomon said, that would not bite like a serpent by stealing away men's brains. In my gift there would be no hidden curse; every good and perfect gift must flow from me.

The jars were ready, the servants waiting uncertainly.

'Now draw some off and take it to the steward,' I said.

As they drew they suddenly burst out in excited chatter. My disciples tasted from a dipping vessel and stared in wide-eyed wonder. Before the guests could start exclaiming over the best-tasting, purest and most wholesome wine they had ever been served, I wanted to get away. My disciples could remain to witness to what they had seen at the Jordan.

As I quietly slipped away, I hoped my disciples had not only had their faith strengthened but would some day understand the symbolism of what they had just witnessed. The water represented baptism into my death, the wine the shedding of my blood for the world. The water had been brought by humans, but my word alone could work the miracle. Just so, they would be handling my word and rites . . . which would for ever be void of transforming power without my Spirit.

THE TEMPLE CLEARED 10

Ever since the visit in my twelfth year to the temple in Jerusalem, I had been deeply troubled by some of the things I saw there. I mentioned this to John as we walked by the lakeside at Capernaum, where we had come from Cana.

'The temple with its outer court is sacred ground, because it stands for the special presence of God. But they've turned it into a noisy place of business, a market. What could be done outside is being done in the temple courtyard. This destroys all sense of sanctity, of worship.'

'And I believe a lot of fraud and extortion also goes on there, Master. In changing money for the temple shekel the worshippers get short-changed. Not to mention the exorbitant prices charged for the sacrificial animals. And it's common knowledge that the priests get their share of the profits.'

'Well, tomorrow we leave for Jerusalem.'

John shook his head sadly. 'What a pity, Master, that there's nothing we can do about the desecration of the temple. The priests won't listen to anything we might say.'

It would soon be Passover, and my mother, brothers, disciples and I joined a caravan. It became clear from the babble around us that this was more a social than a religious event to most. I did hear some talk about the coming of the Messiah, but it was always based on a partial understanding of Scripture.

On the twelfth day we came within sight of the walled city. I spent much of that night in prayer on the Hill of Olives. What had been revealed to me in Capernaum by the Spirit was reaffirmed. The time had come for me to announce to Jerusalem that *its Messiah had come.*

I heard a crunch of footsteps and saw John approaching. 'Ah, you've found me, John!' I said.

'In the moonlight I saw you coming this way, Master. I fell asleep again. It must have been two or three hours ago.'

'Sit down, John.' He sat down close to me on a rock. 'I was looking across the valley at the temple. Thinking of the sacrifices and the people bringing them.'

The morning sacrifice of a male lamb would already have been made; other offerings would follow. Because of man's tendency to secularize everything in life — indeed, life itself — I had instituted these sacrifices. They were to help man, as constant reminders of eternal truths.

'Master, some people say the sacrifices are a cruel, bloody, inhuman system.'

'Yet nearly all who say that are quite happy to have animals slaughtered so that they can eat them. They don't object to animals being killed. They only object when the killing serves a higher purpose than the satisfaction of their appetites.'

After a brief silence John tried to draw me out by asking, 'A higher purpose?'

'Why do you bring sacrifices, John?'

'Well . . . Moses commanded us to do so, Master.'

'Not a bad answer. But it doesn't go to the heart of the matter, does it?'

'Er, no. God commanded it, Master.'

His faith and insight still fell short of seeing me as the one who spoke to Moses, and to Abraham before Moses.

'Why did God command it?'

'Why?' John looked puzzled. 'Because of sin, Master.'

'Does God like the sight of blood, John?'

He looked at me appealingly and said, 'Please tell me, Master.'

'Remember the words of the prophet Samuel to King Saul, "Do offerings and sacrifices please the Lord as much as obedience? Obedience is better than sacrifice." In the fiftieth Psalm God asks, "Will I eat the flesh of bulls, or drink the blood of goats?" And God says through Isaiah, "To what purpose do you bring a great many sacrifices to me? I am sated with the sacrifice of rams. I take no delight in the blood of bulls or lambs or goats." The idea that God is gratified when you slaughter animals to him is a pagan idea, utterly foreign to his character.'

'But this is — well, not what I was taught, Master. And you have just yourself said that God introduced the sacrificial system.'

'Yes, God did. To what purpose?'

'Was it,' John asked uncertainly, 'for man's sake?'

'It was. In the first place, to remind man of the result of sin — death. By sin — which is rebellion, as Samuel said to Saul — man cuts himself off from God. When he cuts himself off from God he cuts himself off from life — he commits suicide. How can you bring this lesson home to man? Isn't the best way having him confess his sin on the head of an animal, then letting him kill the animal?'

'Ah, yes, Master. And every time the force of the lesson wears off and he sins again, he has to repeat the lesson.'

'I'm very sorry for the poor animals,' I said. 'They were

headed for slaughter anyway, but this hastens their death, poor beasts. The point is that it's all an effort to save man, made in the image of God. It's an object lesson. It not only shows him that sin brings death, but that God in mercy provides a substitute death.'

Would John now remember the Baptist's words, 'There is the Lamb of God that bears the sin of the world'? No. His mind was still groping in the dark on that matter.

'I must go to the temple, John.' I had to show myself as the Messiah, and do so in the right place — the temple.

We made our way down the hill, past the garden called Gethsemane and across the valley. As we neared the temple we could hear the muffled noise from the sacred precincts.

Joined by the other disciples we entered the outer temple court by Shushan Gate. The scene that met our eyes was nightmarish. Here, on grounds belonging to the temple, men were bargaining raucously over money, dragging braying goats and bleating sheep back and forth, shopping around for the cheapest doves. Priests wandered about, keeping a sharp eye on the money changers, joining in arguments about rates of exchange, and steering penitents to dealers in animals.

I saw a cord of rushes lying on one side. Picking it up, I walked through the milling crowd and mounted the fourteen steps of the inner sacred area. From here I could see all of the northern and much of the western sections of the outer court. Dwarfed by the high inner wall behind me, I stood with my back to a gate beyond which were the Court of Israel and the Court of Priests. There men were confessing their sins on animals, their voices drowned in the marketplace din. How lovely the tall colonnaded cloisters all round! How obscene among the worshippers were the superstition, the love of money, and the exploitation of ignorance!

All this buying and selling, this shoving and whining and bluster, focused on just one thing — sacrifices. And in their midst stood the One to whom all these sacrifices pointed — yet to a man, priest and layman alike, they failed to recognize him!

I saw the lame, the blind, the dumb begging for money. Money with which to buy not the food they so obviously needed, but doves. They felt driven by what they had been taught, to sacrifice to a God of whose loving fatherhood they had no conception. The poor, the sick and the dying were pleading for help which no one stopped to offer. It was enough to bring tears to my eyes.

At this moment the Spirit opened future centuries to my mind and I saw an unholy traffic in the things of heaven and the souls of men. On the one hand I saw great prestige, power and wealth, combined with learning; on the other, benighted minds and a tragic misreading of God's character and word. Nothing but the judgement of God could clear away the unsavoury mess.

And today, in symbol, that judgement had come to Jerusalem.

Keeping my eyes on the men below, I braided the cord into a whip. Suddenly eyes were swivelling in my direction. The money-changers seated nearby stared as though they sensed that the Spirit had opened their very thoughts to me. Priests and penitents turned to look. I saw guilt flickering across faces. As my gaze swept over the multitude, silence fell to the farthest colonnade. The Spirit who had come on me in such fullness at the Jordan was making the divine presence felt. I saw men blanch and quail.

All heard as I commanded, 'Clear these things away! Stop making a market of my Father's house!'

Slowly walking down the steps, I raised the whip and overturned the first table, scattering money over the marble paving. Tables crashed, money-men ran. There was a flicker of resistance from the priests, then they panicked and fled. Holding the whip aloft as a symbol of God's judgement, I moved from wall to wall. Men condemned by their consciences saw me coming, grabbed their animals and with cries of terror made their escape. I looked with pity at their fleeing backs, yearning to banish their fear and their ignorance of true worship. Within minutes the outer court was cleared of traders and merchandise.

With coins crunching under my sandals, I walked past my disciples huddled in an awestruck group, and beckoned to the lame, the dumb, the poor. How my heart bled for these unfortunates! Throwing the whip from me and blinking at my tears, I raised both arms.

'Come, my friends! Heaven is closer than you think. You have thought to buy God's blessing. Now come and receive it without money and without price!'

They came, timid, hesitant, beginning to believe and hope.

'Come closer,' I said to my disciples. 'You're amazed at my strange behaviour. Haven't you read the prophetic words in Psalm sixty-nine, "Zeal for God's house has consumed me"?'

I motioned for a blind man to be led forward. 'What do you desire?' I asked.

'Oh, Lord!' he cried, trembling from head to foot. 'Eyes! Eyes that can see!'

'Your eyes can see,' I said, touching them gently.

Those dull eyes suddenly flashed with a world of light. He gasped, stared, went down on shaking knees.

I bent over all of them, old and young. Each was healed of his disease.

While this went on, the priests, money merchants and animal dealers began to drift back. They came closer and stared. There was a man whose legs were just thin twisted sticks. I touched him and his legs at once straightened and were fleshed out by God's power so that he shouted and wept with joy while jumping about. The temple officials and traders saw this miracle and many others, and heard men and women breathlessly telling of their suffering and despair. 'But the Deliverer sent by God has healed me! He is the Messiah!' they heard the common people crying; yet their hearts stayed shut, filled with resentment.

Once again I mounted the fourteen steps and stood looking at the crowd standing shoulder to shoulder, faces raised, some blissful and others sullen but awed.

'Listen to the words of the prophet Malachi,' I said. 'He foretold this day, and another still to come, when he said, "The Lord whom you are expecting will suddenly come to his temple. He is the Messenger of the Covenant who will make you glad, says the Lord of Hosts. Who can endure the day of his coming? Who will be unmoved when he appears? He is like a refiner's fire, like fuller's soap. He will judge, refining and purifying. . . ." .'

I came down the steps and found priests and officials blocking my way. They did not look very brave, but felt they had to make some show of authority.

'What sign,' they asked, 'can you show as authority for your actions?'

They had just seen a conclusive sign . . . and were unwilling to acknowledge it. The guilt that overwhelmed them with panic as they fled from the temple precincts had been proof enough. On top of that they had seen miracle upon miracle. Yet they demanded one more miracle! For such unbelieving hearts I had no word; they only wanted me out of their lives, preferably dead, as they had been saying to one another on their way back to the temple.

I would respond with a parable. A parable that was simple, yet thought-provoking and unforgettable. My enemies would not understand it. They would misconstrue it and eventually use it against me; but for years it would be discussed all through the country and would in the long run help my friends to greater faith.

'Destroy this temple,' I said, 'and in three days I will raise it again.'

'What!' they exclaimed indignantly. 'It has taken forty-six years to build this temple! And you'd raise it again in three days?'

At this moment my eye fell on the important-looking man who had been in the Baptist's audience in the wilderness beyond the Jordan. Yes, I thought as I did when I first saw him, your path and mine will cross — soon.

The crowd parted as I made my way to Shushan Gate. Should I tell the disciples what I meant by the cryptic remark? No, it was too early to depress them with thoughts of my death. And as to the deeper meaning — the end of the earthly priesthood and system of sacrifices at the moment of my death, and how my resurrection on the third day would open the way for me to be man's high priest in the heavenly temple — for this they were as yet quite unprepared.

I turned to John, who pressed in close to me as we walked. 'Well, John, so must the human heart be cleansed of all that defiles. You understand that?' His eyes widened. 'Then the heart becomes the temple of the Spirit.'

NIGHT VISITOR

Over the Passover I spoke to the people and healed the sick in Jerusalem's streets and the temple's now-respected outer court; and returned each night to the humble house on the Hill of Olives where I had been offered hospitality. I saw the important-looking man in my audiences several times, and one night there was a knock at the door and my host, roused from his bed, showed this same man in by the light of a lamp.

'Rabbi Nicodemus,' he said, bowing to the visitor.

The rabbi was nervous. This was a secret visit. He was afraid his colleagues would come to hear of it and treat him with scorn.

'My good man,' he said to my host, 'I'd be deeply, er,

indebted to you if this little visit, which is private and confidential, you understand . . .'

My host bowed again, eager to please, and left.

'Perhaps,' Nicodemus said, 'if we could possibly go on the roof . . . ' He did not want his words overheard, but felt the need to offer a reason with a more dignified sound. 'The moon is so brilliant, so full . . . '

I led the way and we settled ourselves on a bench under a luminous sky. He was an anxious man, as the Spirit had shown me. My cleansing of the temple had roused hatred in the Sanhedrin, and there were plans afoot to kill me. Nicodemus, torn between conflicting loyalties, had been one of the Council members who opposed such schemes. This very day he had said, 'My fellow teachers of Israel, you know how our fathers slew God's prophets, how God sent the Jewish nation into bondage to Babylon because we rejected his reproofs. Are we perhaps repeating history? Should we not allow this man a little time, so that we can be sure we're not fighting against God?'

More important, he had since hearing The Voice in the wilderness been making an open-minded study of the Scriptures on the subject of the Messiah. What he found there, and what he witnessed at my cleansing of the temple, left him convinced that I was the Promised One.

But then, I thought, Satan is also convinced of that.

And that highlights your problem, Rabbi Nicodemus. Conviction is not enough.

He was unsure how to start the conversation. One of the things he had been mulling over on his way up here came to his aid.

'Rabbi,' he said, 'we know that you are a teacher sent by God. No one could do the miraculous signs you have been doing, unless God were with him.'

A compliment, an attempt to ingratiate himself . . . how dismally it fell short of saying, 'I know you are the Messiah'!

Yet this man, I knew, was of that exquisite and rare

breed — a truth-seeker. Was he searching for truth in order merely to put his mind at rest — or to conform his life?

Gently I said, 'I must tell you with all possible emphasis, unless a man is born from above he cannot see the kingdom of God.'

I looked him straight in the eye and he knew the words were meant for him. He was shocked. He, son of Abraham, ordained priest, learned theologian, esteemed member of the Sanhedrin — *he* needed a fundamental change before he could have a place in God's kingdom?

Barely managing to keep the sarcasm out of his voice, he said, 'How can a man be born when he is old? Can he enter his mother's womb a second time and be born?'

So will people ever shelter behind interpretations, Nicodemus. You know in your heart of hearts that I'm not talking about a physical birth, just as you're not speaking about the body when you refer to heathen converts to the faith of Israel as new-born children.

'I cannot stress this too much: No one can enter the kingdom of God without being born from water and the Spirit. Flesh can give birth to nothing but flesh; it takes the Spirit to give birth to spirit. Don't look so shocked, then, at my insistence that you must be born from above. The wind blows where it wills. You hear the sound it makes, but can't tell where it comes from or where it is going. So with everyone who is born of the Spirit.'

How it would have encouraged me if he had exclaimed, 'I want to be reborn from above! This very minute!'

Instead, although some light was beginning to get through, his thinking was still slow and mechanistic, as though the 'how' outweighed the 'I must'.

'How can this happen?' he asked.

'Can you, a prominent teacher of Israel, really be ignorant of such things?' I spoke sadly, and so softly that he leaned closer. 'Let me assure you, we are talking about

55

something we really know. What we tell you we have actually observed. Yet all of you reject our testimony.'

He had started off by saying I was from God. 'If you don't believe when I tell you about experiences here on earth, what chance is there that you'll believe me when I describe heavenly things? No witness on earth has been to heaven — except the Son of Man whose home is in heaven.'

I was indeed the Son of Man; yet I alone among men had firsthand knowledge of heaven, because heaven was my home.

Nicodemus's face was radiant. He was beginning to believe in a new way — with the first stirrings of a desire to be reborn of the Spirit. But he would not now take his stand. He was too cautious by nature. The idea of witnessing publicly to a repentance which no one thought he needed — least of all himself before tonight — by stepping down into the water of baptism, was something before which his pride recoiled. He would only be able to take the final courageous step when he saw me crucified. To help his faith then, I must prime him with a prophetic assurance now.

'The Son of Man must be lifted higher than the heads of men' — my crucifixion — 'as Moses lifted up the serpent in the desert' — those who in faith looked at the bronze snake on the pole were saved from the poisonous snakes at their feet — 'so that anyone who has faith in him may have eternal life.'

We looked each other steadily in the eye. As a theologian he knew that the bronze serpent had no power to save those bitten by snakes. The serpent was a symbol of the Deliverer, the One who would come from God. I was saying I was that Deliverer.

Was I also saying that as the bronze serpent was made in the image of the snakes, so the Deliver from heaven would come among men as a man — as the Son of Man? I was indeed, but I would leave the question in his mind. It was something about which he could exercise his soul in prayer.

When he left, John, who had been awakened by the arrival of our visitor and had overheard part of the conversation, wanted to know more. He listened carefully to what I told him, without grasping the significance of all I had said to Nicodemus. But I could see that he was overwhelmed by the concept of God's love. He was seeing for the first time that God was actually *giving* the One who stood in such a special relationship to him, so that every true believer in him should, instead of being lost, have eternal life.

'Will Rabbi Nicodemus now be a disciple of yours, Master?' he asked.

'He will befriend us in the Sanhedrin. Later he will cast in his lot with us. By so doing he will lose a great deal . . . and gain everything.'

IN JUDEA 12

As crowds streamed to us daily, excitement built up among my five disciples. It is interesting to watch how popularity transports people to a heaven of euphoria. It inflates their ego and puts a sparkle in their personality, without in the least increasing their intrinsic worth. Burst the bubble of their popularity and at once they are shattered. This is one of the symptoms of how frothily superficial man's sense of values has become.

One day after seeing yet again how the blind were given sight, the lame mobility, the diseased health, Peter could no longer contain his feelings. With the crowd still streaming after us as we left Jerusalem, he came up with a confiding air.

'Master, there is something about which I — we — must speak to you. It's the question of what to do next. Perhaps you are thinking at this very time — that is, if you think, as we do, that this is the time . . . '

'Yes, Peter?'

His rugged face took on a sage look. 'The miracle at Cana, Master — we were very impressed. But it was a private occasion. Now, the cleansing of the temple was another matter. Hundreds of people saw it with their own eyes. And there were priests among them, leaders of the nation, wealthy men, educated men — even members of the Sanhedrin. When they saw you performing all those miracles of healing directly afterwards, it added to the powerful impression made. Now, what with Rabbi Nicodemus inclining our way, as are some other leading men, and while the impression of the signs which you did today is fresh upon everybody, we wonder if the time isn't ripe . . . '

The rest of the disciples were now also crowding closer, nodding, eager of eye.

I sighed. 'You want me to go to the Sanhedrin?'

'Exactly, Master! If they accept you as the One sent by God, and throw in their weight with us — who can stop us? Why, the whole nation would join us!'

'And what should I say to the Sanhedrin, Peter?'

'Well, I don't know, Master. You will know. They just need to be convinced that you are the Messiah — the rest will follow.'

'And how do I convince them, Peter?'

For a moment his face was blank. 'Well, Master, a sign, a miracle . . . ' He shrugged.

'Peter — after what sign or miracle did you cast in your lot with me?'

He was nonplussed. We walked on in silence. Satan had asked me for signs and miracles after the forty days' fast. And the priests who fled from the temple drifted back to witness miracle upon miracle . . . then demanded a sign.

The next morning I preached again at the temple and in the streets of Jerusalem, but I knew this would be my last day. The feasts of Passover and Pentecost were past, the pilgrims had gone home, and the people of Jerusalem were more agog over my miracles than my message.

To the great disappointment of my disciples I left Jerusalem and moved northwards. Still in Judea, I carried on my work among the towns and villages, aware that everything I did and said was at once reported to the Sanhedrin in the capital. This was their chance, free from the pressure of my turning Jerusalem upside down all about them, to study the prophecies with hearts open to the interpretation of the Spirit.

So important was this chance extended to the priests and rabbis, that I was prepared to give them ample time by witnessing within reach of Jerusalem for a full year. For eight months I worked from village to village, sometimes with only one disciple because the others had gone back to their homes and businesses to give some support to their families. By then it was clear that virtually all the priests and rabbis had decided against me.

If the Sanhedrin felt threatened by me, John the Baptist had even more reason for such feelings. Whereas a year earlier he had been the most sought-after man in Israel, able to command an army if he had announced himself as the Messiah and declared war on Rome, I had by now taken over most of his followers.

This became acutely clear by the winter of that year. He was baptizing at Aenon, near to Salim, because water was plentiful in that region, when my disciples and I in our wanderings arrived in the same area. We had large audiences, swelled even further when half of John's people also flocked to us.

Many people presented themselves for baptism, and I continued to set my seal on John's baptism by having my disciples baptize them. A leading religionist from Jerusalem was present at one of our baptismal occasions. He and his friends at once rushed to John's disciples to foment trouble between John and me.

'Why is the teacher from Nazareth also baptizing?' he asked. 'You got the practice from our Jewish custom of baptizing proselytes from heathenism for their purification, didn't you? But then why baptize Jews? This is an insult! Or did your leader get it from that little clan of Essenes near the Dead Sea? To them it's also symbolic of purification. Yet there are vital differences between your baptism and theirs. And what about the words used at your baptism? How do they compare with those used by the Nazarene's disciples? And what about daily ritual washings? . . . '

The devil's work was done, and soon John's disciples were locked in argument with mine, finally challenging their right to baptize at all.

John's disciples reported the matter to him and said, 'Master, the man who was with you on the other side of the Jordan, the one you pointed out, is now also baptizing. And the crowds are flocking to him!'

My old adversary was behind this. John's work was declining, but everywhere he was held in the highest esteem as a man of God. If he uttered one disgruntled word that might be interpreted against me, he could harm my work. Satan was putting him under pressure from his beloved, faithful disciples, trying to provoke him to jealousy.

John hesitated. He had been watching his followers leaving to join me.

'The Nazarene is taking over your work, Master! You're being pushed into the background, after all you've done for him! If it goes on like this, you'll soon have nothing left. Can't you get him to leave all the baptizing to you? After all, you started it! Why should you be treated like this?'

John hesitated no longer. He raised his hand to stop their flow of words. 'My dear, dear friends, the success I had came from heaven. His greater success also comes from God! Didn't I tell you, "I am not the Messiah, only the one sent as his forerunner"?'

His unselfishness took the wind out of their sails.

'It is the bridegroom who gets the bride, my friends. Yet the bridegroom's friend who helped to arrange the marriage is overjoyed at the happiness he hears in the bridegroom's voice. I couldn't be happier!'

Then he said something that brought tears to my eyes when it was reported to me: 'He must grow greater, and I must grow less.'

'The one who has come from above, is above all others,' said John. 'The one whose origins are earthly, can only witness on an earthly level. He who comes from heaven can speak about the higher things he has seen and heard. Yet no one is truly accepting him in that context. Anyone doing so would be vindicating and honouring God! The One sent by God speaks on God's behalf, out of the fullness of the Spirit. The Father loves the Son and has left everything in his hands. He who has an enduring faith in the Son has a hold on eternal life. Those disobedient to the Son will not see that life but come under divine wrath.'

John spoke with amazing insight: 'no one' was truly accepting me. Audiences flocked to me, there were droves of sick people every day, and my name was on everyone's lips. But I was too poor and too humble to be quite the divine, pre-existent Messiah, except to a few . . .

For the moment John's selfless firmness had quashed attempts to divide us, but the enemy would not rest.

JUST A SAMARITAN WOMAN 13

My disciples were still asleep when I quietly rose and picked my way under the stars to an open field. Frost lay white on the ground and the raw winter's morning chilled me to the marrow, but that was not why I shuddered. I was thinking of what lay ahead for my noble 'Voice in the Wilderness', John the Baptist. And the horror would start within four months.

Deeply moved, I prayed for him, for strength and faithfulness to the end. Then I prayed for the people of Judea whom I was leaving behind. They had been a disappointment. There had been no lack of crowds, of enthusiasm, of loud praising of God as I healed the sick under the guidance and power of the Spirit. But I knew how superficial this excitement was. I had worked in Jerusalem and most of Judea for one thing — changed lives. Lives renewed from above; lives to which the divine nature had been imparted, leading to characters touched with holiness. And measured by this standard my work had been a relative failure.

As I was earnestly praying, two comforting assurances came to me. The Spirit showed me that my work in Judea would help to produce a harvest of thousands one day. Moreover, that I was soon to meet a Samaritan woman who was ready for the kingdom. Some secret details of her life were revealed to me.

I returned to my disciples and after breakfasting on the last food we had, we set off for Galilee. Jews travelling between Judea and Galilee normally took the longer route east of the Jordan to avoid Samaritan country; I raised my disciples' eyebrows by heading due north.

For more than five hours I stretched my legs so vigorously that they sweated to keep up. By noon we reached the ancient well of Jacob, near Sychar.

'Well, if you're as hungry and parched as I am . . . ' I said, halting and mopping my brow.

'We do have a little money, Master,' said John, flopping to the ground. 'We could buy some food in that village.'

'Hm, Samaritan food,' Peter grunted. 'Well, it's in order to take food from them so long as we pay for it and don't accept it as a gift.'

'Can anyone tell me how we can get some water out of this well?' Andrew asked, staring longingly down the shaft. Interesting . . . he did not turn to me for a miracle, to bring the water surging to the top. He did not know that I had decided never to work a miracle on my own behalf, yet instinctively refrained from asking what I would refuse.

While they went in search of food I sat on one of the stones ringing the well. Nearby rose Mount Gerizim, considered sacred by the Samaritans. The hatred between Samaritan and Jew went back five hundred years to the time when Cyrus the Great allowed the exiles to return to Jerusalem. The Jews destroyed the Samaritans' temple on Gerizim one and a half centuries ago, and detested them so much that all social dealings with them were condemned. Even to borrow from a Samaritan or accept a favour from one was out of the question.

I hoped my disciples would get a drink in the village and not need to wait for water to be drawn here. My throat was painfully parched and I felt enervated by hunger and the long hike.

I might easily have sat till late afternoon, normal water-drawing time; but the woman appeared. She was humming to herself, pot secure on her head, gait lissome, noticing from a distance that I was not a Samaritan and tactfully ignoring me. An arm's length away she paid out her rope. Far below there was the soft splash and she started hauling up. Coiling the rope over her shoulder, she was about to lift the dripping jar to her head when I said, 'Please give me to drink.'

She was startled. 'How can you, a Jew, ask of a Samaritan woman the gift of a drink?'

I smiled. Yes, this could make me a pariah to the Jews.

She now had her hand on her hip, saucy, bantering.

'If you only knew God's Gift,' I said earnestly, 'and who it is that is asking you for a drink, you would have asked him and he would have given you living water.'

Mystified and sobered she said, 'Sir, you have nothing to draw water with and this well is deep. How could you get at your living water? Are you a greater man than Jacob our ancestor, who gave us the well and with his family and animals drank from it?' She was still thinking of this water. Jacob drank of it and died, so who was I, talking about so-called 'living water'?

'Anyone who drinks this water will be thirsty again. Whoever drinks the water that I can provide will never again suffer thirst. The water I provide will be an inner spring, ever welling up for eternal life.'

Now she knew that my water had nothing to do with Jacob's Well. 'Sir, give me that water so I won't get thirsty and have to come here to draw water!'

A pathetic eagerness, holding great promise for the future — but she was still thinking only of her physical and material needs. Needing to bring her up short with a sense of her spiritual need, I said, 'Fetch your husband.'

She hesitated. 'I don't have a husband.'

'You are quite right in saying you have no husband. You have had five husbands and the man you're living with is not your husband. What you say is true.'

Shock showed in her eyes and her hand went to her throat. 'I — I see you're a prophet, sir,' she said unsteadily, under the misapprehension that prophets are all-knowing. She was desperate to change the subject, start an argument, anything to get off the subject of the men in her life. 'Our forefathers worshipped on this mountain, but you Jews say the place where men should worship is in Jerusalem.'

The passionate emphasis people place on externals, at the cost of heart-religion, has to be met with gentle firmness.

'Believe me, the time is coming when your worship of the Father must be without reference to this mountain or Jerusalem.'

I thought of the images these people used in their worship. They protested that this was no violation of my commandment against bowing before graven images. The images, they claimed, were mere aids to the devout imagination. I knew better. 'You are worshipping without true knowledge. We worship with a clearer insight, for salvation is by way of the Jews.'

She would not at once understand what I meant by this — the Scriptures and the Messiah appearing in the lineage of Abraham. But she had observed my lack of prejudice against Samaritans; and what she must be helped to see was the need to come to grips with her prejudice against everything Jewish.

Behind her I saw my disciples approaching, John in advance of the others and already within earshot.

'The time is coming, in fact has come, when those who are real worshippers will worship the Father in spirit and in truth. The Father is searching for that quality of worshipper. God is spirit, and those who worship him must worship in spirit and in truth.'

She looked at me, hesitating on the threshold of an overpowering thought. 'I know the Messiah is coming. When he comes he will make everything plain to us.' She was timid, almost frightened of the thought which the Spirit was urging on her.

'I am he — *I who am speaking to you.*'

John was now at her side. The others came up, all showing surprise at my readiness to talk to a woman in public — and a Samaritan at that.

I watched her face. She believed! The Christ was here! And she had talked with him!

She turned and dashed off to tell others, leaving her water pot behind.

I bowed my head. She did not know it, but the living water was already there, springing up in her for other souls. She was on her way to call others to me. At this stage all she could say would be, 'Come out and see a man who has told me everything I ever did! Could he be the Anointed?'

I sat there praying for her and for her friends, then stared at scenes presented before my mind's eye — scenes of rejoicing in heaven over this one sinner who was turning to

God. How little do people know of the realities of heaven! They have no grasp of how universal the attention is that is focused on this tiny planet. The cosmic issues involved in man's destiny escape them. If only they could see how the news of this woman's faith had just been flashed all through heaven!

She would persevere, I knew. A great unfolding of a new life was taking place while we watched. Here was a miracle of God's grace indeed, beside which the physical healings in Judea paled into insignificance . . . because the healed body dies later anyway. A new life had just come from above, and it glowed with an unearthly beauty.

'Master,' John was saying softly, as though afraid to intrude. 'We've brought bread, dried fruit. Do eat something.'

She would have a new expression on her face, a new sound in her voice. 'Come and see! Isn't he the Messiah?' They would stare, hardly knowing her. She would tug at their sleeves, point. 'You've got to meet him! Come and look for yourselves!' They would come — they were coming — as fast as their legs would carry them.

'Master, you're famished. Do have something.'

My thirst and hunger had been overwhelmed by joy. 'I have food to eat of which you know nothing.'

Andrew whispered to Peter, 'Do you think somebody brought him food?'

I sighed. 'My food is doing the will of him who sent me, until I have finished his work.'

Beyond them I saw the first contingent of Samaritans tearing along towards us. How could anyone think of eating when famished souls needed feeding? I waved at the fields of grain across the way, a sea of fresh green.

'You'll say it's about four months to harvest time. Is it really four months off?' I pointed to the approaching crowd, of which they had been unaware till this moment.

'Look, I tell you, there are the fields! They're ripe and ready for harvesting.'

And you, my five apprentices, were about to participate in a glorious reaping where I had done the sowing. 'Here comes the reaper's reward — a crop for eternal life! Sower and reaper are going to rejoice together. And in this there lies a truism: One sows, another reaps. Where others have toiled you will get the harvest.'

They arrived, out of breath, staring as I rose to give them a smiling welcome.

'Sir,' one ventured, gulping for breath, 'the woman — oh, there's her water jar still — told us you knew all about her private life . . . '

'Didn't I tell her something incomparably more important?'

They crowded round, keen to know about the Messiah, listening carefully to my replies, wanting texts in the books of Moses — the only Scriptures they had — explained. More groups arrived — how hard that woman was working in the village! — and explanations had to be repeated.

Urging us to spend the night with them, they set food before us and to my disciples' acute discomfort, almost consternation, I accepted the Samaritans' hospitality. This was learning time — for my chauvinistic disciples as much as for the Samaritans.

THE ARISTOCRAT'S SON   14

'Master, why are we skirting Nazareth?' John asked.

'The people there do not believe in me. Remember this: a prophet is not appreciated in his own country.'

When we got to Cana in Galilee I was received with enthusiasm. In their midst the first miracle had been seen, and some of them had been in Jerusalem nine months ago when I cleared the temple and healed hundreds of sufferers.

The Spirit had shown me how the news of my arrival reached a prominent Jewish royal official at Capernaum, five hours on foot from Cana. His young son had been given up by his doctors and lapsed into a feverish coma. 'I must go and plead with this Jesus to come here,' he told his wife; who protested, 'But our son will be dead by the time you get back! You must be with him, with me, when he dies!' 'I've a better chance of getting Jesus here if I go myself.' 'But do you believe in him?' 'They say he's the Messiah, but I won't believe in him unless he does for me what I ask. Seeing is believing.'

And there he was, for a while unable to get to me through the Cana crowd. An hour after noon I was making my way to the shade of a tree when one of my disciples said an important man from Capernaum wanted to speak to me.

'Greetings, sir,' he said with taut politeness, deeply dismayed to find me poor and travel-worn. He hesitated, faith faltering, until he thought of his son. 'I am from Capernaum, where my son lies at death's door. I have heard a great deal about you. Could you, possibly . . . ?'

'Will you never believe without preconditions? Must there be a miracle, must it be "seeing is believing"?'

He clutched at the tree with a trembling hand, shaken because I knew his thoughts. A glimmer of understanding broke through to him. He saw the selfishness of his motives, realized that his unbelief imperilled his son's life.

'Master,' he said when he could speak, 'my son is dying! You *can* give him life! Please come! Please!'

'Go home. Your son will live.'

The greater miracle was the way he accepted my refusal to accompany him, and was content with my assurance. He could have been home that evening, but now he was in no hurry. He believed, stayed all afternoon to listen, and learned that the sign of my Messiahship lay not in miracles but in the quality of my teachings.

Next morning, on the outskirts of Capernaum his servants shouted to him, 'Master, your son is well!'

He merely nodded. 'And when did he get well?'

'Master, an hour after noon yesterday he could hardly take another breath. Suddenly his fever was gone, he sat up bright-eyed, then fell into a healthy sleep!'

His son, glowing with health, met him at the door, and there he broke down and wept on his knees. From that moment he gathered all possible information about me. He and his family became my followers, and with their witness prepared the way for the work I was to launch in Capernaum six months later.

BETHESDA — REJECTION! 15

We arrived in Jerusalem on Yom Chamishi, the fifth day of the week. The next day was Eve-of-Sabbath, and early in the morning I went to Bethesda, the so-called Sheep Pool. There were already at least two hundred invalids lying about under the surrounding colonnades. We stood watching them — people in various stages of paralysis, people blind and dumb, sufferers from all kinds of disabling and painful diseases. All the sighted among them faced the pool, waiting.

Suddenly a bubble burst on the surface and a great shout went up. A stampede started for the water, mad and strange. They wriggled, lurched, clawed at the paving stones, while those unable to move cried pathetically for someone to have mercy on them and throw them in the water. Near the edge two were trampled by stronger men as about thirty slithered and toppled into the water.

'They believe it's an angel who stirs the water, and the first one in gets cured,' Nathanael said.

When it was all over the two who had been trampled and nearly killed were dragged away from the edge. Sometimes men died there.

'Do you want to make them all well, Master?' Nathanael was almost rubbing his hands in anticipation.

I nodded. 'Of course. But let us move on.'

He followed, disappointed. I knew better than to step down to Bethesda and make all those people well. All that was needed was one word; but the Spirit had shown me that if I did perform this mass healing it would sweep the people off their feet. They would take me by force to declare me their King, and enraged priests and rabbis would have Pilate's soldiers sent in to break up what they would brand an insurrection against Rome, and in the melee the religious leaders and their henchmen would try to kill me by knife-thrust or a well-aimed rock. My work must not be cut short; I must not play into my adversary's hands.

I had been spotted and a commotion was breaking out as my name rang in the narrow streets and masses of people descended on us.

'Master, Master!' a garlic-breathed, round-faced man shouted in my ear. 'Yesterday when you arrived they were selling animals and changing money in the temple court. Today they're all gone, afraid of you!'

Yes, after my departure a year ago they had gone back to making the temple court a money-grubbing market.

The next day was the Sabbath.

'Let us go to Bethesda,' I said.

A remarkable number of sick people crowded the pool. They did not know me, having been unable to join the crowds that followed me, and it was refreshing to pick my way among them without being recognized. Who was the most hopeless case here? I had been praying about this and would know the man.

Here he was, wretched beyond description, legs useless, body emaciated, one arm shrivelled up. He had been a helpless cripple for thirty-eight years. Not only did he suffer from disease and malnutrition, but also in his conscience — this was, he felt, a judgement from God because his life of sin had been largely responsible for this malady. On top of all his misery was the fact that thirty-eight years of being little better than a vegetable had weakened his mind.

He took no notice of Nathanael and me, but raised his head occasionally from his mat to gaze at the pool. I bent over him.

'Do you want to get well?' I asked.

He opened dull eyes, in which a semblance of hope showed for a moment before the lids sagged back. There were flies on his bedsores and he smelled. He rolled his head away from me.

'There's nobody. When the water moves.' It was like a wheeze, the words flowing together. 'To put me in. Others step on me.'

He opened his bloodshot eyes and blinked into my face. The blinking stopped as he read my expression. I would depart from my preferred procedure and not expect faith before I acted.

Softly, in the love of heaven, I said, 'Get up, take up your bed, and walk.'

For a second the words seemed to have no meaning for him. He could, if he wanted to, simply close his eyes with a tired sigh, shutting me out. I nodded encouragement. Holding my gaze he set himself for a blind spasm of obedience.

He stood erect, the shrivelled arm levering straight and strong against the paving. Where no flesh had been apparent, muscles rippled smoothly. The bedsores were gone. He came up in such an ecstasy of vigour that he was on his toes, arms raised as though to fly, eyes locked in mine.

I had tried to draw no attention, but cries of shock and amazement were beginning to go up. I caught Nathanael's eye and moved off briskly.

'Master! What about the rest of them?' Nathanael protested breathlessly at my elbow.

'He was the worst.'

For a while the cured paralytic was beside himself with joy. Then he remembered the command which God had given through me. Rolling up his mat and blanket he put the roll under one arm and marched off. Soon he spotted some priests. Bubbling over with praise, he went to them.

'Do you recognize me, the man paralysed for thirty-eight years, the man who lay at Bethesda?' he exulted. 'A man cured me! Look at me! Look at my legs, my arms! Isn't God good? Isn't God great?'

To his surprise they frowned coldly.

'Who is the man who cured you?' they demanded, knowing full well but eager to get testimony against me of a Sabbath miracle.

'Who? I don't know, but what does that matter? I'm cured! Cured, that's the thing that counts. Cured after thirty-eight years of suffering! Aren't you going to rejoice with me?'

They were not. 'Why are you carrying your pallet on the Sabbath? Don't you know it's not allowed?'

'The Sabbath? I don't know what day it is. After thirty-eight years of not moving, all days feel the same. I'm carrying this because the man who cured me told me to take up my rug and walk.'

'He told you to carry that, did he?'

'He did.'

They pushed him aside and hurried to Bethesda to lay hands on me. My new 'preacher' went on his way catching every eye with his roll of bedding, as my Father had intended. He attracted an audience as honey attracts ants, and witnessed left and right till Jerusalem resounded with wonder and praise.

I was addressing an audience from steps in the temple's outer court two days later, on Yom Sheni, when I saw another crowd cascading through a gateway towards us. In the middle was my friend, excitedly answering questions about his thirty-eight years and the instant of healing.

To my audience I said, 'The people that lived in darkness have seen a great light. Those living in the land of the shadow of death have been flooded with light.' With these words from Isaiah's prophecy of the child born to be called Wonderful Counsellor, Mighty God, Everlasting Father and Prince of Peace, I left the steps and moved through the crush of people to my preacher's side. He had a sin offering and a thank offering — from somewhere he had obtained flour, bread and a lamb. Becoming aware of me, he broke off in midsentence.

I left him with his crowd, from whom he learned who I was. Overjoyed, he at once sought out the priests who had challenged him on the Sabbath day.

'It was Jesus of Nazareth who cured me two days ago!' he exclaimed, thinking this would put the whole matter right.

My enemies were ready for me when I deliberately returned to the temple an hour later. Joseph Caiaphas the high priest and most of his Sanhedrin were in place, not in their private chamber in the Court of Israel, but just inside Shushan Gate where the crowds could witness everything. I heard cries of 'There he is!' and then four men were steering me towards where the onlookers had been cleared back from the imposing judges on their ornate chairs.

'Are you Jesus of Nazareth?' a priest standing near Caiaphas snapped at me.

'I am.'

'Do you recognize this man?'

It was my poor preacher, trembling between two officials.

'I do.'

'Did you tell him two days ago to break the Sabbath by bearing a burden?' I heard the hiss of indrawn breath from the crowd.

'How could I tell a man paralysed for thirty-eight years to pick up an object and walk with it?' I asked. 'Could you, or the high priest behind you?'

He gritted his teeth: the Sanhedrin would have preferred no mention of the miracle. An excited humming came from the people.

'All right then, a second charge. Did you cure this man on the Sabbath?'

'Do you admit that he was a helpless paralytic for thirty-eight years and that the temple and its priests had no help to offer him?'

The man's fury was as great as that of my adversary when on the mountain I refused his offer of all the world's greatness.

'Did you or did you not break the Sabbath and incite another to do the same?' he screamed.

'To cite the prophet Isaiah, whom you revere, "I cannot tolerate your Sabbaths and assemblies, your sacred seasons and ceremonies." Would you stone Isaiah for writing such words, or God for speaking them in the first place? You ask whether I broke the Sabbath. Shall I accept your traditions which pervert the Sabbath and conflict with God's mind? You legislate that it is a desecration of the Sabbath to treat a chronically sick person, to spit on the ground lest you "irrigate" a blade of grass, to eat an egg laid on the Sabbath. Isaiah says, "Woe unto those who make laws without merit, who prescribe burdensome decrees." I say it is right to cure the suffering on the Sabbath. It is also right to testify to that cure by word . . . and by the proof of action called for by heaven. Your man-made traditions are of no value in God's sight!

'You, whose very prayers Isaiah calls an abomination to God because your hands are full of the blood of hatred, would forbid God himself to cure a sufferer on the Sabbath! Yet God goes on healing seven days a week, and he it was who did so two days ago at Bethesda!

'God's special work is saving work — redemption. This he never stops for a single day. So I say to you: My Father has never yet ceased His work, and I am involved in the same work!'

Howls of outrage burst from my prosecutor and the men behind him. They understood all too well what I meant.

'He's calling God his own Father! He's claiming equality with God!' they shouted, sowing confusion and consternation in many a mind.

The Sanhedrin members were on their feet, ready to stone me to death. But they found themselves faced by a very large crowd, the bulk of whom did not share their feelings, and fear held them back.

I raised my hand. Silence fell.

'Listen carefully to my words. I assure you, the Son does *nothing* of his own accord. He acts only as he sees the Father acting. Father and Son collaborate.' That applied to the act of healing, and to the bedroll. Furthermore, the very words I was speaking came as much from the Father as from me.

'The Father loves the Son, shows him all he does, and will amaze you with greater deeds yet. For just as the Father raises the dead to life, so the Son gives life to men, as he determines. And the Father judges no one, having put judgement entirely into the Son's hands. This means all must pay the Son the same honour as that given to the Father. To deny honour to the Son is to deny it to the Father who sent him.'

I had turned so that I was facing the crowd more than my sacerdotal accusers.

'I tell you emphatically, anyone who gives heed to what I say and puts his trust in him who sent me has eternal life! Judgement will not overtake him: he has already passed from the realm of death to that of life. I assure you, a time is coming, and in a sense is already here, when the dead shall hear the voice of the Son of God, and all who hear it shall come to life. For just as the Father has life in himself, so has the Son, by the Father's gift.

'As Son of Man, the right to pass judgement has been committed to him. Do not let this astound you. The time is coming when all who are in the grave shall hear his voice and come out. Those who have done right will share in the resurrection that brings life; those who have done wrong will rise in the resurrection of doom.

'Not that I act independently in this. I judge justly, in harmony with the will of him who sent me, my aim ever being not to do my own will.'

The massed crowd listened in total silence, ready to accept if left alone by the religious leaders. But they had a superstitious regard for these leaders; most of them were well caught in the web of human tradition which these men and former generations like them had woven.

I glanced at the priests and rabbis. Two were hard at work on one side, writing down my words at a furious pace. All were avid for words with which I would seal my own doom.

Before the Sanhedrin and the people, in the shadow of Jerusalem's temple, I was officially announcing my divine status as the long-expected Messiah. And my claims were about to be officially rejected.

'Because I am bearing testimony on my own behalf, you will consider it worthless testimony. There is another who bears witness for me, and I know that his witness is trustworthy.

'Your deputation went to John and you have his testimony to the truth. Not that I rely on human testimony, but I point this out in the interests of your salvation. John certainly was a brightly-burning lamp, and for a while you basked in his light.

'But I have a more exalted testimony than John's. The work which my Father gave me to carry to completion, the very works to which I am devoted, provide enough testimony that the Father has sent me. And the Father who sent me has himself also spoken on my behalf. You have never heard his voice, seen his person, or allowed his word to live in you, as can be seen in the fact that you do not believe the one whom he sent! You search the Scriptures, convinced that you will find eternal life in them. These very Scriptures bear testimony to me, yet you refuse to come to me for that life!'

The accused had become accuser. The one who never spent a day in their schools was indicting the most highly educated men in the country before the temple crowd. I was not railing against them with human passion, a passion which they so easily indulged. As I rebuked them for the hardness of their hearts and their superficial understanding of the Scriptures, they heard love's pleading in my voice. They still had a chance. I did not ask to be esteemed by them; I wanted them to have eternal life.

'To receive glory from you is a matter of indifference to me, because I know only too well that you lack true love for God. I have come in my Father's name, yet you do not accept me. If another should come in his own name, you would welcome him! How can you believe in me while you are obsessed with receiving honour from one another? While you do not seek the glory that comes from him who alone is God?

'Do not imagine that I shall accuse you to the Father. Your accuser is . . . Moses! Yes, the very man on whom you have set your hope! If you really believed Moses you would believe me, for it was about me that he wrote. But if you do not believe what he wrote, how can you believe what I say?'

I examined the faces of the crowd, looked my rigid-faced priestly enemies over, turned and headed for Shushan Gate. Not a voice or a hand was raised to stop me. Halfway through the gate I said to Nathanael, 'You should stay and see for yourself what is about to happen.'

I was passing through the Kidron Valley when the high priest delivered his verdict to the people.

'We find Jesus of Nazareth guilty of curing a man on the Sabbath. We find him guilty of sacrilege. Infinitely greater, however, is the sin of blasphemy, for he makes himself equal with God. We warn you, he is an impostor and a false prophet! Have no dealings with him, as you value your souls! Keep to the religion of your fathers and so safeguard yourselves from deadly error!'

They sent messengers all over the country to carry this warning everywhere. Determined to take my life, they dispatched spies to report on my actions and every word I uttered.

I had been officially rejected.

TO GALILEE

Before nightfall the news reached me that John, the man who baptized me, had been arrested. I strode off alone along the summit of the Hill of Olives, thinking of him.

His addresses could rightly be called sermons, because they made his audiences sit up with a 'What must we *do*?' They cut to the quick of conscience. John could condone nothing that was below standard — and his standard was not a human one but that set by God. Many a man or woman who said to him, 'I believe. Now, what must I *do*?' found John ready to give instruction in godly living, and ready even to demolish any idols set up in the inquirer's heart.

Herod Antipas, ruler of Galilee and Perea and the son of Herod 'the Great' who killed the babies in Bethlehem, had heard about John and wanted to meet him. While travelling through Perea he summoned the prophet, listened to his message and felt conscience-stricken. 'Prophet, what must I do to be right with God?' he asked privately. 'God's message to Your Majesty is, "Give me your heart." ' 'What about my marriage?' 'You have no right to your brother's wife,' John said fearlessly.

Herod did make some feeble efforts to get out of Herodias's toils, but she knew how to play on his weaknesses. When her grip on him was strong enough she persuaded him to arrest the prophet who had dared to offer advice opposed to her interests. He intended to release the great man later — without taking account of his own fatal flaws of character.

From now on the Baptist was moving inexorably towards a gruesome death. He who had breathed the free air of the wilds, who had spent two years in active service for me, was chained in a dark, dank dungeon where life passed him by. My heart bled for him. It was some consolation to know that he would escape the second death by having eternal life; and in a quaint way it was also a comfort to reflect that my fate in this life would be worse than his.

Because John's disciples in the northern and eastern areas were now without a shepherd, I wanted to leave without delay.

It was to Galilee that Nathanael and I went — Galilee, despised by the religious leaders of Jerusalem as a province of rustics. Having found them less hidebound, more open to Scriptural persuasion, and more earnest than the people of Judea, I looked forward to a year of hard work among them.

I went from village to village, town to town. Usually I began speaking to only one or two people, but soon passers-by would stop to listen and ask questions. Gradually an audience would build up, sometimes a milling multitude. Before leaving any town, I healed the sick. As the word spread, people came from as far afield as Judea to hear God made understandable.

Often a crowd, witnessing miracles such as the one at Bethesda, threatened to get out of hand with excitement. Then I withdrew to isolated places until the feelings had cooled.

The science of salvation — this was my daily topic. And

it all revolved round the acts of God in and through the Messiah. All through the Scriptures I unfolded it, in the books of Moses, the prophets, the general writings, revealing the Messiah in the symbols of sacrifices, first-born sons, priesthood, sanctuary services, manna, brass serpent, burning bush, and in specific promises and prophecies. In the revelation of truth, heaven was brought down to men. Never had there been such a period as this for the world.

Often I quoted the words which Gabriel spoke to the prophet Daniel, 'Seventy weeks are cut off and set aside for your nation and your holy city, to fill up the measure of their rebellion, to end sin offerings, to atone for sins, to provide for everlasting righteousness, to confirm the vision and prophecy, and to anoint the Most Holy.'

'Now,' I told them, 'the time specified is fulfilled. The measure of rebellion is nearly full, the time just before us when sin offerings will cease. Atonement will soon be made. God's kingdom of grace is at hand!'

For this reason I called, as the Baptist had done, for repentance. God's love demanded that he give everything for men's salvation, and this he was doing before their very eyes. Their grateful love for God demanded that they give everything to the Lifegiver and Lifebringer.

Many did this. Moved not so much by the miracles of healing which they saw, as by the revelation of divine truth, they gave themselves heart and soul to God.

My work in less-esteemed Galilee was far more fruitful than that in Judea. I felt fortified against what I knew awaited me in that other town of Galilee — Nazareth.

NAZARETH'S VERDICT 17

From the Plain of Esdraelon I followed the narrow track up the winding ravine, remembering how as a child I had clambered about on these rocks. All this had once been a big new world of discovery to me, a world of birds, tortoises, lizards, wild flowers, of being alone in nature with thoughts like tendrils groping Godward.

Nathanael would not be visiting Nazareth with me, having gone to his home town Cana and from there on to Capernaum. I wondered how Andrew and John were faring, and Peter and Philip — and that other John, my beloved forerunner, in prison. Here I was, entrusted with a cosmic mission, nerved with a sense of life-and-death urgency . . . a lonely, dusty figure trudging up a mountain track. In prayer for others, I took heart and pressed on up the hill to Nazareth.

There it was, nestling in its pear-shaped depression among the hills. Beloved village, beloved people! Simple folk, yet some highly talented. Musical talents, voice and instruments. Social talents, charm, conversational prowess. Artisans who were artists. Loafers, bullies, the decadent and criminal. The religious and the worldly. I had to swallow against the nostalgia that rose in me.

A shrunken little man leading a donkey recognized me. 'Hey, Yeshua!' he called, hand up to wave.

'Muppim!' A few long strides and I embraced him, glowing with joy to see him again.

'A long time,' he said simply.

'I've been gone nineteen months, Muppim.'

A dear man, slow and faithful, with never an unkind word for a soul. As poor as could be.

'I've heard . . . things about you.'

'Tolerably good things, I hope, Muppim. How is your health?'

'No complaints, no complaints.' How typical of him, under all circumstances. 'You know how your family are?'

'No, I'd like to know.'

'Still the same, still the same.'

I was moving on a few minutes later when he cleared his throat.

'Yeshua, I — I've always liked you.' He was embarrassed.

'I think, er, you could be, you likely could be . . . the Promised One.'

'Besides my mother, you're the only one in this town who believes that, Muppim.'

It was a precious moment that I cherished as I made my way into the village. There were hearty greetings, inquisitive stares, a general friendliness; but no further word of confidence in my mission. Not even among my family. My mother was tearfully happy, my sisters shy and delighted, my brothers pleased, each in their own way. James was serious and thoughtful, Joses jovially back-slapping, Simon full of banter, and Judas — whom I called Jude — bubbling with questions about my long months from home.

Sabbath morning came, with an air of expectancy. People streamed to the synagogue, today not just as a meritorious act — as they thought of it — but hoping for some excitement. My mother and sisters sat with their children on backless benches on one side, I with my brothers on the men's side, all of us facing the ark while conscious of the many eyes turning to the new arrival in town. I reflected on how I had never missed a Sabbath in this unpretentious synagogue during all my years in Nazareth, and what an oasis of peace that day had always been for me in a taxing week. Often, even as a child, I had been asked to read the lesson from the Prophets, as had others of my age; and I had always tried hard to let new light shine out of the sacred words. Today the challenge was going to be infinitely greater.

The service started. The shema. We recited our confession of faith; a prayer was offered. The parashah. The words of Moses were read by seven men in turn. The haphtarah. The president was going to do it himself; everyone had expected that this was where he would call on me. He had a set, determined look on his round face. The dire warnings against me had reached him from Jerusalem. He was going to speak about the Messiah and set the matter straight, unmasking me. He read from Jeremiah.

'Behold, the days are coming, says the Lord, when I will

raise up for David a righteous Branch, who will reign as King, wisely and well, and enforce law and justice in the land. Under him Judah will be saved and Israel live in security. And this is the name by which he will be called: "The Lord is our righteousness." '

He cleared his throat. 'When the Messiah appears, he will be a great and glorious King, saving Judah, occupying the throne of David. This glorious and royal King *has not yet come.*'

That was enough. All could see I was a pretender, not the promised Majesty. My confusion should now be demonstrated to all. He fastened his gaze on me and said, 'We shall repeat the haphtarah. Yeshua bar Yoseph will read.'

I rose slowly, made my way forward, past the front seats where the rich and important sat. The chazzan raised his eyebrows.

'The book of Isaiah,' I said.

He went to the ark, found the scroll, removed the cover. At the reader's desk I unrolled the scroll most of the way, looked over the massed faces, and read the Hebrew.

'The Spirit of the Lord God is upon me, because the Lord has anointed me. He has sent me to preach good news to the humble, to bind up those whose hearts are broken, to proclaim liberty to the captives and the opening of the eyes to those who are bound, to proclaim the year of the Lord's favour . . . '

I stopped there for two reasons. The next phrase, 'the day of the vengeance of our God', belonged to the second coming of the Messiah, not the first. Secondly, my audience delighted to dwell on 'the vengeance of our God' as something which would fall on the Gentiles in general and the Romans in particular, but not on the descendants of Abraham, Isaac and Jacob; and I did not want to trigger their self-righteous reaction.

Turning a short distance back in the scroll, I read, 'Is not this the kind of fasting that I require of you: to loose the shackles of injustice, to undo the thongs of the yoke, to set free those who are crushed, to shatter every yoke?'

Rerolling the scroll I handed it to the chazzan who returned it to the ark. I sat down in the seat of Moses. The president met my gaze with a frown, the front-benchers stared intently, the ordinary folk gaped. My mother's hand was at her throat, appeal in her eyes.

I said, 'As our esteemed president read to us, the Lord promised through Jeremiah that we should have a King on David's throne. The King and indeed the throne seem conspicuously absent. Yet I want to say this: the promised Messiah will be in the line of David, and he will be a King!' There was a breathless hush in the synagogue. 'That is not the question. You look for him to be a King in Jerusalem, ruling Israel and driving out the Romans. I expect him to be more than this. I expect him to be King over the whole world, for Isaiah says, "Of the increase of his government and peace there shall be no end." Do you believe that? That the Messiah's kingdom will be endless and without limits?'

Their eyes shone. So they would, after all, have a King! And one of the very kind they wanted.

'But *when* will the Messiah be King? The Preacher, son of King David, says, "To everything there is an appointed time, a time for every purpose under the heavens." Before the Messiah comes as King of kings and Lord of lords, he must come in a more difficult, more demanding and arduous ministry.

'As I read from Isaiah, the Messiah will preach good news to the humble, bind up those whose hearts are broken, proclaim liberty to the captives and the opening of the eyes to those bound about with darkness, set free those who are crushed, and announce the time of the Lord's grace. The humble? Yes, he will be close to the humble, a friend to the poor.

'He will bind up those whose hearts are broken. He will proclaim liberty to those taken captive by Satan. At his word the blind will see. He will set free those who are bruised and crushed under man-made burdens never required by God. He will announce the time of God's release to a new life. He will be your friend, your helper, your redeemer. Is this the kind of Messiah you want?'

They uttered fervent amens, some prodding others and glowing, 'But he's just Joseph's son, isn't he? Where does he get it all from?' Even in the front rows there were minute nods.

'Today this scripture is fulfilled before you!' I said, and saw the startlement turning every face rigid. 'The humble have heard the good news, in Jerusalem, in Judea, in Galilee. The brokenhearted have been given a new lease on life. Israel is in bondage to that greatest of all oppressions, sin. They have heard liberty proclaimed to them, as you are hearing it at this moment. The blind have had their sight restored — as all may have, who are yet blind to what heaven is trying to show them!'

They were sullen now, smarting under the suggestion that they might be under the power of darkness and in need of light.

'Do you feel crushed by life?' I was pleading with them. 'Accept the freedom offered you! Have you been trying to serve God but you feel overwhelmed by a mass of man-imposed requirements with which you are supposed to win God's favour? Dear friends, give God your hearts today and you will be free!'

One thought was dinning in their minds: If you want us to believe in you, work one of the miracles about which we've been hearing so much! What about that miracle of the boy who was dying at Capernaum? You've been saving others — now save yourself, in our estimation! Miracles, miracles!

The only miracle I was prepared to give them was to show that I read their thoughts.

'No doubt you will quote the proverb to me, "Physician heal yourself!" You are saying, "What we have heard you did in Capernaum, do here in your own town also!" ' The shot went home — their faces showed it. They had their sign. And they rejected it, glaring angrily.

'I assure you,' I said in sorrow, 'no prophet is recognized in his own country. Consider these facts. There were many widows in Israel in Elijah's time, when for three years and six months the skies never opened, and famine lay hard over the whole country. Yet Elijah was not sent to a single one of them. Where was he sent? Out among the Gentiles, to a widow at Sarepta in the territory of Sidon! Again, there were a great many lepers in Israel in the time of the prophet Elisha. Not one of them was healed, except Naaman the Syrian.'

'What!' The president was on his feet, trembling with anger. 'Are you saying God favours the Gentiles above Israel? The unholy above the chosen? Young Yeshua, you're nothing but a traitor to your own nation!' Behind him there were mutters of rage as men surged to their feet.

'Answer the president, answer the president!' men yelled.

'This is my answer: God esteems the believing heart above the unbelieving heart.'

'He's saying Israel has departed from God!' screamed the president, throwing up his arms.

I tried to speak, but my words were drowned in a tumult. They rushed at me, one or two slipping and falling, being trampled. I remained calmly in the seat of Moses. Rough hands laid hold of me, lifting me off the seat and off my feet.

'Kill the Gentile-lover!' a hoarse voice shouted.

'Kill him, kill him!'

'Traitor! Traitor!'

They tugged at me, trying to wrench an arm from a socket.

'Not in the synagogue!' screamed the president.

'No, the Precipice, the Precipice!'

My adversary was driving these poor people mad,

convinced he could cut short my work, sure that I had put myself into his hands by assuming frail human nature.

I would on no account use divine power to escape. Even less would I retaliate, not by so much as a thought. I had come to serve others, not myself, and would do nothing on my own behalf.

'Here it is! Stand back, open the way!'

'Let's stone him first!'

They gave way round me, and as I picked myself up a stone narrowly missed my head. I was in my Father's hands. The moment had come for him to act.

I saw men blinking blankly, unable to see me. Those nearest were silent, groping unsteadily, while the rest still bellowed insanely.

I walked with measured tread through the crowd. Men were recoiling, whimpering, arms out defensively, a nameless judgement-day fear on their faces.

Rejected by my own people, I took the road to Capernaum.

CALL BY THE SEA 18

It was a sad night on the lake of Galilee for the seven men. Not only did their nets bring up nothing, but four of them, John, James, Andrew and Peter, were deeply depressed about the prospects of my work.

'It was started wrong,' mourned Peter. 'The Master should first have gone all out to win over the religious leaders. Then everything would have been plain sailing. To launch out preaching without recognizing their authority was to antagonize them. The result is they've declared war on the whole thing. That's why we had such poor results in Judea. Everything is dead against the Master now.'

The others agreed that I had started unwisely. 'Look at the Baptist,' Peter complained. 'In prison. Six months already.

Abandoned. If this is the fate of a really godly man like him, what hope is there for the rest of us? In a way we had no choice but to leave the Master's work to come and fend for our families.'

'Not much good that's doing us, with the nets coming up empty every time,' said John from the other boat.

'Everything's gone wrong,' Peter lamented.

Day eventually began to break. 'We'll have to leave it now,' said Andrew.

'But neither boat has caught a single fish all night!' Peter exploded. 'How are we going to feed our families?'

'Well, in this clear water we've got no hope of catching fish by day.'

They gave up and started for shore.

'Look at that, it's the Master!' John shouted.

I had come down early to be alone before the crowds gathered, but already people had discovered me and were coming at a run — peasants and fishermen, merchants and even some rabbis. Soon the crowd was so unwieldy that I felt mobbed. The two boats landed just beyond the throng and with an effort I made my way there and got into Peter's boat as the men were starting to wash their nets.

'Push off a little, Peter,' I suggested. We moved out a short way. I sat down and addressed the crowd for an hour. How I yearned over these dear well-disposed people, and over others like them as my mind's eye saw them in ages to come.

Then I turned to the two brothers in my boat. 'Andrew, Peter, push out into deeper water and let down your nets for a catch.'

'But Master, it's hopeless!' Peter exclaimed. 'We've been slaving away at it all night. Not a fish.'

'Well, do it once more.'

'But it's light now, Master. In this clear water the fish evade our nets and anyway by day they lie too deep . . . ' He saw my expression, looked at Andrew, shrugged, 'But if you say so . . . '

The nets were let down, and minutes later they were giving way under the weight of fish. Peter shouted for help, and at once the men on the beach dropped the nets they were mending and launched their boat.

The men battled, the boats rocked and rode lower and lower in the water as the fish were piled in.

'Lord!' Peter cried, falling down and clutching my feet. 'Get away from me, I'm a sinful man!'

'Don't give way so easily to discouragement, Peter. From now on your catch will be people.'

They beached the two boats. Helped by the two hired hands and Zebedee, father of James and John, the four got the enormous catch to land.

'Has it struck you what this means?' I asked. 'God can supply all your needs — for the rest of your lives. Have faith in God, dear friends. Moreover, God will provide the catch for his kingdom, as you henceforth work only for him.'

I looked at Peter, Andrew, John and James. They had seen their own impotence and would trust less to themselves than in the past. How vital that was!

This was the moment. They must never again go back to secular work.

'Follow me, and I will make you fishers of men,' I said. Turning my back on them, I moved off purposefully.

Leaving boats and fish, capital and income, they at once came after me.

INSANITY IN A SYNAGOGUE 19

At the home of the Jewish court official we were made welcome, first by the boy whose life had been saved and then by his parents.

'It is half a year since you spoke the word at Cana, Lord — the word that cured my son on his death-bed here in Capernaum,' the man said reverently.

'I will never forget it as long as I live,' said his wife.

'And I will keep on telling everyone about it, Lord,' the boy assured me.

He was only 13. 'What do you tell the people, Zuriel?' I asked.

'I tell them I believe you are the Messiah, Lord.'

'A political messiah?'

'Political? I don't . . . '

'There have been quite a few of those recently,' said his father. 'And the people flock to them. Zealous, patriotic men these political deliverers are, too. They've been arrested one after another, these men who try to mobilize us against the government.' He reflected for a moment and shook his head. 'They've given the very idea of the Messiah a bad name.'

I looked at my disciples, hoping this thought would lodge in their minds. Yes, the very word 'Messiah' was enough in this district nowadays to make the Romans' blood boil, and during my crowd-filled weeks in Capernaum I had avoided open claims to Messiahship.

'Lord,' said the official a little later, 'no one will come on a Sabbath to be cured of his or her sickness. The rabbis have intimidated them. But I hear a lot of talk that they will be coming to you just after sunset, when the Sabbath has ended.'

Spring was merging into summer, and the Sabbath dawned brilliant with sunlight. The synagogue was full to overflowing as I spoke.

When I finished, the people wanted more and I went on, watching the play of emotions on their faces. What a light shone in some eyes! A whole new world was opening before them.

Other faces wore a frown, the eyes were cold, and I felt a deep and almost despairing concern.

Using simple illustrations I tried to make clear the principles of God's kingdom, especially the principle of love. Although I did not strive for emotional effect, many an eye grew moist, and I silently thanked my Father for bringing heaven in touch with earth.

At this point my adversary was ready. He had brought a man to the synagogue who was now just outside, eyeing the choked doorway. He heard my voice, and it brought added confusion to the chaos of his mind. Certain words excited him, but he could concentrate for only an instant before other voices inside his skull clamoured for attention. My adversary gave a final order to the rebel angel in charge of this poor derelict of humanity.

At once the man launched himself towards the doorway. With superhuman strength he thrust about ten people aside, stopped for a moment as he caught sight of me in front, then ploughed his way forward, starting to show flecks of froth at the corners of his mouth.

'A demon-possessed man!' someone screamed.

'It is the love of God that frees you from the captivity of darkness,' I had just said.

I stood waiting for him. Everyone seemed to stop breathing. Hefty men got out of his way. Hunched and grunting, arms flailing, eyes red and glaring, he was coming straight at me.

As I looked him steadily in the eye, his impetus wavered. With clutching hands outstretched towards me he halted, breathing hard, lips drawn back from his teeth.

'Yes?' I said gently.

A terrible struggle was going on in his soul. Years ago he had decided to experiment with anything that offered excitement, not stopping to think that this would pervert and deprave him, locking him into a dependence that made him an easy prey for Satan. Now a glimmer of light was breaking through to that enslaved mind and he wanted to call out the word, 'Help!'

He opened his mouth and out rushed the words, 'What have we got to do with you, Jesus of Nazareth?' His face and hands were working and every syllable was a tortured growl.

'You've come to destroy us! I know who you are — the Holy One of God!'

Very clever, seeing that there were spies of the Romans right here, ready to report on Messianic claims so that I could be arrested like the others in this region who had aspired to the title and tried to lead the people in revolts that proved self-destructive.

'Be silent,' I commanded. 'And come out of him!'

I was face to face with my adversary who had offered me all the kingdoms of this world if I would pay him homage. He threw the man down, screaming and in convulsions. That masterly mind had in a flash decided to kill his victim, to make the people shrink from me in terror. I had been talking of love; now they would see my word as a prelude to a violent death! The maniac said I came to destroy — *now the proof, his own corpse, would be provided!*

'Let go of him at once!' I ordered.

A shuddering shriek and it was all over. The man lay still. I stepped forward and lifted him. He was dazed, but his eyes cleared and he sank to his knees in sobbing relief and praise.

All over there were cries of amazement. 'What on earth is this!' 'It's a new religion with power!' 'Even unclean spirits obey his orders!'

I calmed the excitement by going on with the service. When it was over, feeling tired, I left with a final word of courage and admonition to the man who had been set free of spirit domination.

At the home of Peter we found that his mother-in-law had in the past hour or two fallen prey to a terrible fever and was close to slipping into a coma. Peter was stunned at the unexpectedness of it, and with others crowded her bedside. It was clear to all that this raging illness could soon sweep the poor woman out of this life.

I rebuked the disease and helped her to sit up. Like

someone who had just woken from sleep, she set about cheerfully serving us food.

The day continued busy, and just after sunset virtually the whole town descended on us with their sick, whom I made well. In expelling demons from their victims I silenced their proclamations of my Messiahship, both because I did not need my adversary's testimony and to thwart their efforts to focus the Romans' heavy-handed attention on me. It was a day to remember, a day resonant with joy and triumph.

THE FIRST LEPER

My days were filled with teaching, my predominant theme being the kingdom of God.

It was here already, full of divine grace that granted forgiveness and produced a new life. Again and again during the following weeks I was overjoyed to see men, women and young people born into that new life.

'You are a citizen of the kingdom,' I said to a man named Thomas in one village. He had been following me about for two weeks, sceptical, tenaciously holding on to his prejudices, yet deeply impressed by what he heard. Then, very suddenly, he was kneeling before me, lips quivering.

Knowing that he was a man of sluggish faith, at times even obstinate unbelief, but also that he was capable of ardent devotion, I said, 'You will be my disciple.'

Nathanael was again following me, and Philip. There were now seven of the twelve I intended.

In the course of my tour of Galilee I marked James, son of Alphaeus, for discipleship, as well as another James's son, Judas. Both, with their faults, were simple, earnest, teachable men.

'You will follow me,' I said to another man, putting my hand on his shoulder. He was called Simon, a man of dangerously fiery spirit against the Romans, a patriot who would need much help lest he imperil my cause with a political zeal for which I had no time.

Peter had been watching my selection of disciples and, typically, decided to have a hand in the matter. Behind my back he gathered earlier recruits, Andrew, James, John, Philip and Nathanael, for a committee meeting.

'We've all seen that it would have been much better to have gone to the religious leaders first,' he said. 'At that stage their prejudices weren't aroused. The Master could have convinced them that he is the Promised One. His words and miracles would have been enough. I'm sure they would have sanctioned his work, backed him. Then we wouldn't have had such an uphill battle in Judea. There would have been no rejection by Jerusalem, no warnings sent out, no spies following us about.'

He seemed not to realize that he was implying a lack of contact on my part with heavenly wisdom. His natural charm and forcefulness disarmed any disquiet that particularly John might have tended to feel.

'But there's somebody following us about who could be a great help to us. With his talents we could repair some of the damage.'

'The tall, big fellow?' James nodded.

'Impressive, isn't he?' said Peter admiringly. 'What personality! And accomplishments! Business experience, brain power, ability to handle people. What a man!'

John was envious. 'He makes me feel small. His name is Judas Iscariot, isn't it?'

'It is. Can I go to the Master on our behalf and advise him to take this man on as a disciple?'

'Not merely advise — strongly urge, I should think,' said Philip.

Peter came with the proposal, not mentioning how disappointed they felt with my poor tactics. I listened carefully and surprised Peter by my cool reception of the idea.

'One only needs to look at him, Lord,' he urged. 'A born leader. A resourceful man. Experienced, talented. A great man. A man who could surprise us!'

The Spirit had opened Judas Iscariot's life to me, and I made no response to Peter's words. But a few days later the man himself came to me and said with pathetic eagerness, 'Master, I will follow you wherever you go!'

I responded as I always did to such words, but this time with a starker emphasis, 'Foxes have their holes, the birds have their roosts, but the Son of Man has nowhere to lay his head.'

Judas Iscariot was attracted to me, but was also consumed with ambition. What with these crowds and my miracles, he thought it just a matter of time until I was ruler of a liberated nation.

'Please, Master, will you accept me?' he begged.

How can I ever, while the Spirit pleads with men, refuse anyone who comes to me?

And so I said, 'If that is what you want,' and Judas became my disciple, to the great joy and relief of the others and some restoration of their faith in my judgement.

Time and again while teaching the people I had seen lepers at a distance trying to make out what was happening. On such occasions I always raised my voice so that they might hear some of the message. Once or twice they ventured closer and were chased off. At the end of the day when they moved off, calling out 'Unclean! Unclean!' as the law required, to warn everyone to keep his distance, I could weep for them.

The Jews considered leprosy a judgement from God because of sin. It was the very symbol of sin — disfiguring, contagious, deadly. You did not touch lepers, nor breathe the air that had passed through their lungs. They had to be banished, shunned, and dreaded.

One day at the lakeside I saw a leper watching us, and recognized him from other days. Fascinated, he was near the edge of the crowd on a rocky rise, intent on my words. For an hour he listened without anyone's turning and catching sight of him. Then he saw the dying laid at my feet and walking away well, the blind given sight, the paralysed jumping up and down; and his heart pounded uncontrollably in that poor body.

He was being drawn by the Holy Spirit, drawn by divine love . . . but would he come?

He clambered off the rock, hesitated, stared longingly. Then he was coming. On the fringe of the crowd shrieks went up and the cry '*Leper!*' Within a moment or two the entire crowd had given way left and right and pandemonium reigned.

'Get away, you living death!' they roared.

They were looking for stones. He kept coming, hobbling on a foot without toes, open sores on his legs, a hand ashen and shrivelled, an ear eaten away, skin scaly. My disciples scattered.

Dropping to those swollen knees he pleaded, 'Master, if you want to you can cleanse me!'

What moved me most was that he meant cleansing from sin and guilt, with his physical condition secondary. Without a moment's hesitation I put out my hand and touched him.

'I want to. Be clean!' I said, meaning in body and soul.

At once the glow of health was all over his body and he was as normal as any awestruck onlooker.

Now there was a problem. I wanted no publicity.

He was stammering a 'Lord! Thank you, thank you, *thank you!*' when I said with stern earnestness, 'Mind you say nothing to anybody! Go to Jerusalem right away, show yourself to the priest and make the offering laid down by Moses so that you can be certified cured.'

One of the results of the ex-leper's ebullient witnessing was a broad-based deputation of my learned enemies. They came to Capernaum, nowadays known as my headquarters, from Jerusalem, Judea and Galilee; and arrived while I was on the other side of the lake. I was shown their deadly purpose. They would have to be defeated.

The healing of the paralysed man at Bethesda four months ago still rankled in their minds. They had not seen it happen, but wherever they went people talked about it. Now, to crown it, there was the case of the leper! But the Bethesda miracle was the turning point, the event that led to my official rejection by them and their colleagues; and they were set on driving the matter to a head and getting me killed.

My reply would be another 'Pool of Bethesda' case — this time before their very eyes. Once more it would be a man who had brought the infection and disease on himself by dissolute living. But in this instance the paralysed man was deeply impressed with his guilt, until forgiveness was his one and only yearning.

The Spirit led him to Capernaum, carried on his stretcher by four men. Discovering that I was still out of town, and that there was an august group of rabbis also waiting for me, he had himself carried to them.

He appealed to them. Some had seen him in previous years when in his restless search for help he appeared stretcher-borne on their doorsteps. They knew his illness and its causes. Looking at his emaciated body and putre-fying sores, there was nothing the deputation could do. This was the hand of God. A deserved curse had struck the man. They told him so, and could only advise him to rest his soul in God, offering him no assurance that brought peace.

I got into a boat and came to Capernaum.

At once the town was agog and people flocked to Peter's

house to stare and listen. Within ten minutes the house was packed, and outside they stood shoulder-to-shoulder.

The committee of rabbis arrived. Such important people could not be left outside. The crowd parted for them, people inside the house being called out and the learned men given seats of honour facing my disciples and me.

The paralysed man arrived on his stretcher, and the crowd did not open for him. He was in despair. His friends pleaded with people and tried to force their way in, to no avail.

'Look!' the paralysed man whispered. 'The roof! Please!'

They took him round the side to the wooden steps set against the wall, with utmost difficulty manhandled him up to the flat roof, and dug up the tiles and earth and broke away the lathwork to make a hole.

Inside, we were showered with debris. Then the stretcher was angled through and let down between me and the theologians, whose expressions grew rigid as they saw who it was. There he lay, saying nothing but staring at me in an agony of appeal.

Deeply moved at this man's plight and hunger for forgiveness, I said gently, 'Your sins are forgiven,' and called him 'my son' to emphasize his acceptance by the Father.

His face became radiant with peace and joy.

My adversaries were shocked. 'This is pure blasphemy,' they thought. 'How can this fellow say things like that? Only God can forgive sins!'

To help them believe, I told them what was in their minds. Then I said, 'You're also thinking how easy it is to tell a paralysed man his sins are forgiven — an invisible matter. Now, which is easier for *you* — to say to this paralysed man, "Your sins are forgiven", or to say, "Stand up, take your bed, and walk"?' Both were impossible for them, as they well knew. 'To convince you that the Son of Man has the right on earth to forgive sins' — I turned to the paralysed man — 'I say to you, stand up, take your bed, and go home.'

He bounded up, all traces of his disease gone, while the witnesses sat stunned. Then he took his stretcher and the awed crowd made way for him.

I looked at Judas Iscariot. His eyes were full of adoration.

LEVI MATTHEW

I knew about Levi Matthew the tax collector, having seen him at the healing of the paralysed man and in illuminations of the Spirit. I felt an affinity with him, on two counts. Isaiah had written about me as the one who would be despised and rejected by men, and Matthew was despised and rejected by his own nation. And he had such a rare open heart for truth.

As a tax man he was regarded as a traitor to his own people, an agent of Rome. And since all tax collectors were considered extortioners who enriched themselves at the expense of the poor, he was thought vile, a man to shun. To me he was a jewel.

I saw him sitting at his toll booth in Capernaum one day. His eyes were on me. As I approached he shrank into himself. Rabbis would spit when they passed him, and to him I was a rabbi. He lowered his gaze to the street and, with a heart at once bounding and quailing, waited for me to pass. How he longed to know me better, to talk about the sins of which he felt so painfully convicted lately; and how numbly sure he felt that although I might not spit, I'd pass him by.

I stopped. He looked up slowly, eyes very wide.

'Matthew, son of Alphaeus,' I said softly, 'follow me.'

I turned and walked on. He sat transfixed for a moment, then jumped up and, leaving his lucrative business behind forever, bounded to catch up with me. I did not look at him for a minute because my heart and eyes were too full. He was trusting God to provide for his family. What faith! I put my arm over his shoulder as we walked on together.

HUNGER

The affinity and the hostility, I thought, looking at the Sabbath crowd. We had made a field close to their village our place of worship, and hour after hour I taught them because they refused to disperse. But among the eager were those not keen to learn and be blessed; their eagerness was to find me guilty of a word or an act.

By mid-afternoon I was very tired. My disciples were both fatigued and hungry: not a morsel had passed our lips in eight hours. Even the audience was near exhaustion, and I suggested that they go home for a rest and some food.

We were walking through a grainfield towards the village when some of my disciples plucked a few ears, rubbed out the kernels and ate them. At once my enemies pounced.

'Look at this!' they cried. 'Why are they doing what is forbidden on the Sabbath?' Their voices were strident: there had to be many witnesses.

I halted and faced my tormentors, learned champions of God. How I yearned to have them see things as God sees them! I looked them over, seeing the handkerchiefs with one end sewn to their robes. Loose, the handkerchiefs would be a 'burden' carried on the Sabbath, desecrating the holy day! Two or three stitches tacking them to a garment and suddenly they were no longer handkerchiefs but part of your clothing!

Dear Father, how man's touch perverts everything we bring into being! How he pictures the Almighty and Omniscient as a tricky being who surrounds his creatures with thousands of rules, and if they innocently break one rule he explodes in anger! A God who lives for formulae, who is charmed by rote and ceremony, whose wrath can be averted by cleverness, who is satisfied with a mechanistic outward religion from which the loving heart is gone! They have taken the beautiful Sabbath which we made for them as a day of glorious uninterrupted communion with their loving Creator, and turned it into a farce!

I would reason with these men from the Scriptures.

'Have you never read what David did, when he and his men were hungry and had nothing to eat? Haven't you read how he went into the house of God at the time when Abiathar was high priest, and with his men ate the bread which had been dedicated to a holy use — bread which only a priest could eat?'

My tone and expression posed the sharp question, *'Do you condemn King David?'*

Their faces showed how unthinkable it was for them to speak a word against David. By their silence they were saying that David's eating of the holy bread was justified by his hunger.

These men, at once learned and ignorant in the Scriptures, needed another analogy.

'And haven't you ever read in the law of Moses how the priests on duty in the temple may work on the Sabbath without incurring blame? I tell you, you are in a presence here greater than the temple!'

In this matter I spoke with absolute authority, 'For the Son of Man is Lord even of the Sabbath,' I told them.

I saw the hatred in their eyes. By declaring myself the owner and sovereign of the Sabbath, I had in their eyes made myself guilty of the highest sacrilege, giving myself the status of Creator. For this they would see me dead.

How I yearned for their salvation! In deep sorrow edged with rebuke, I said, 'If you had grasped the meaning of the verse of Scripture, *"I require mercy more than sacrifice"*, you would not have been so quick to condemn those who aren't guilty!'

Would they see it when next they read Hosea? See that

an outward religion of rites, ceremonies and good deeds, without the warm, pulsing heart of love for God and man, is an offence to God?

As we walked on I prayed that these men of God's service might see it and be converted.

THE PERSECUTORS

24

'Love your enemies,' I told my listeners on more than one occasion. 'Bless those who curse you. Hate only one thing — sin. Love the sinner, and in that sense you will be perfect, like your Father in heaven.'

I was never persecuted by the worldly, the atheist or agnostic, the religious sceptic or godless. Indeed, the irreligious seemed fascinated by my life and ideas, and utterly awed by my miracles.

The hatred and persecution came from the zealously religious, especially the learned leaders, the professional men of God.

In the synagogue on the Sabbath I looked at them. They sat close together, following my every move, exchanging whispered comments, unspontaneous, grim. Under other circumstances these men could smile and display a hearty sense of humour — something I keenly appreciated. They were good husbands and fathers, men of prayer and morality . . . and men of prejudice, of preconceived interpretation, of professional jealousy, of hatred.

They sat there like a depressing cloud surrounded by bright sunshine, and my heart yearned over them. How could I help these men? I had come to die for them. Was there any way, any way at all, in which I could help them to eternal life?

'A question,' one of them said, standing up.

I often read from Isaiah, and had just read the words, 'Thus says the Lord: "Keep justice and do righteousness, for my salvation will soon come, my deliverance soon be revealed. Blessed is the man who does this, and the son of man who holds to is, who keeps the Sabbath without profaning it, and keeps his distance from evil." ' I inclined my head to receive the rabbi's question, knowing what it would be, having prepared the way for it.

'Is it permitted to heal on the Sabbath day?'

I had seen them glancing at a man with his right arm shrivelled up, the hand dangling close to his chest. I was being challenged; there was a trap yawning at my feet.

'Come and stand out here,' I invited the unfortunate man. He got up and came forward.

'Is it right to do good or to do evil on the Sabbath, to save life . . . *or to kill?*'

My questioner sat down. Neither he nor his friends had any relish for a discussion — every debate they had tried had ended in disaster. And the way I said 'or to kill' showed them that I knew how they had broken this very Sabbath by plotting how to kill me. Any moment I might have revealed to the audience that they were profaners of the holy day. How strange — the Sabbath-breakers were eager to find me guilty of Sabbath-breaking! They were confusing divine commands with human laws to accuse *me*, the only one who could say, 'I have *kept* my Father's commandments'!

But I would not betray them; I'd appeal to them with all possible love and reasonableness.

'Suppose one of you had a sheep which fell into a ditch on the Sabbath. Would you leave it to die? Or would you set to work and haul it out?'

Some glared at me, others put their heads back and stared pointedly at the ceiling. In their stubborn prejudice they were unwilling to say a word in favour of God's mercy! A feeling of anger rose in me, anger at Satan's misrepresentations of God's gracious character; then it gave way to grief that these poor men were listening to the wrong voice and holding eternal life at a distance from themselves and those who listened to them.

They *would* save the animal, to avoid financial loss. 'Surely,' I pleaded, 'a man is worth far more than a sheep!' Still they wouldn't respond. 'It is therefore *right* to do *good* on the Sabbath.'

I turned to the man. 'Stretch out your arm.'

Believing in my word, my power, he did so. At once his right arm and hand were as sound as his left.

As the exclamations of wonder and awe broke out among the congregation, the religious leaders got up and stalked out. While the service was still in progress they began to plot with the supporters of King Herod — Herod, whom they normally detested! — on ways of putting an end to my life.

TRUE HAPPINESS 25

To allow things to simmer down I left the town after the Sabbath. The next day we were at the lake of Galilee. Soon a large number of people gathered, crowding and touching me to such an extent that I had Peter keep a boat ready from which I could speak to those on shore. I healed their sick, strictly admonishing them not to talk about this too much. Demon-possessed people also crossed my path, falling down and crying 'You are the Son of God!' to confuse the crowd and make them think we were in league. I rejected their testimony and silenced them.

The work was now growing big enough to need some organization. In preparation for this, after a tiring day I left my disciples and a group of persistent followers at the foot of a hill and spent the entire night alone in prayer near the summit. At the first light of dawn I went down part of the way and called the others up.

The twelve disciples were anything but impressive. None were members of the Jewish aristocracy. All were poor

— even Matthew since abandoning his lucrative business. All except Matthew and Judas Iscariot could virtually be called illiterate, uncultured, uncouth.

But eleven of them were highly promising learners. Three would become able writers, including Matthew. John would become a profound scholar.

About to appoint them to the most important service ever given to men, I called them out one at a time. I said, 'You will be my specially-sent ones, my apostles. You will represent me. You will preach the Gospel of the heavenly kingdom. At the same time you will heal the sick and cast out demons.'

I knelt with them around me, laid my hands on each head in turn, dedicating and ordaining them to my sacred work.

Now I was ready to proclaim to them the constitution of my kingdom. But down below a crowd had gathered, I knew, and they were milling about like sheep without a shepherd. They should hear the principles of the kingdom expounded to the apostles.

We went down to the narrow lakeside and found it under such a crush of people that I had to lead them some way back up the hill, where they sat on a stretch of level ground and I could sit overlooking them and the lake below.

How many would cherish what I was about to tell them? How many would know that they were hearing the most important words uttered since the proclamation on that other mountain, Sinai?

My disciples pressed in close to me. Was I about to announce that my kingdom was taking over this part of the world? There was an air of expectancy all through the crowd. They wanted the Romans out. Those church leaders and spies — they wanted nothing less than a takeover of the Roman empire with all its wealth and glory!

I had not come to bring victory over enemies, national glory, cradle-to-grave security and luxury. I could offer them victory over selfishness and sin. I could offer them glory of character. I could hold before them endless life, vigorous and fascinating life in an Eden restored. My mission was not temporary advantage, but an eternal weight of glory. And this they could only receive on condition that they accepted the principles of the kingdom.

Looking into those hundreds of bright, eager eyes, I began to enunciate those principles:

'True happiness comes to the humble, those who know how much they need God; the kingdom of heaven is theirs.

'True happiness comes to those who mourn over sin and repent; they shall be comforted.

'True happiness comes to those who are gentle, self-controlled; the earth shall be their possession.

'True happiness comes to those who hunger and thirst to obey God's will in thought, word and deed; they shall be satisfied.

'True happiness comes to those who show mercy; mercy shall be shown them.

'True happiness comes to those with purity of mind and character; they shall see God.

'True happiness comes to those who work for peace towards God and towards mankind; God shall call them his children.

'True happiness comes to those who reflect the character of God; they will be persecuted, but the kingdom of heaven is theirs. True happiness comes to those who suffer insults and persecution and every kind of calumny for my sake. Be glad, in fact rejoice, for you have a rich reward in heaven. In the same way they persecuted the prophets before you.'

They were almost breathlessly intent on every word, awakening to the fact that I was not talking about political kingdoms and earthly benefits. How I longed that they might all at this moment enter the Kingdom of Grace, in preparation for the day when I would come to make them part of the Kingdom of Glory!

To be in the kingdom of grace they must accept me as the promised Christ. More yet: *they must be living representatives of my kingdom.* To accept me without accepting my life as a standard for their own, would be like using tasteless salt in food; or like hiding a light where it will not dispel darkness.

But to some my life stood for flouting of a certain class of law — man-made laws, which they easily confused with divine law. It would never do for them to think of me as a transgressor of God's law. How could such a thought be entertained for a moment concerning the one of whom Scripture prophesied, 'I delight to do your will, O my God; yes, your law is in my heart'?

So I said with emphasis, 'Never think that I have come to take away the Law or the Prophets! I have not come to abolish them, but that they might fully come into their own. I assure you, while heaven and earth last, and until all is accomplished, the Law will not change in the tiniest detail. Whoever tampers with the least of the Law's commandments and teaches others accordingly, will be disdained in the kingdom of heaven. On the other hand, anyone who keeps the Law and teaches others so will be highly regarded in the kingdom of heaven. I tell you, unless your righteousness is of a far higher quality than that of the Pharisees and the doctors of the law, you can never enter the kingdom of heaven!'

I had not come to make God's law more remote, but to bring it closer home to my followers. To illustrate this I pointed to the commandment of the great moral law prohibiting murder. You do not break this commandment only when you kill somebody, I said. You are already breaking it when you nurse anger against somebody, or when you insult him. Such a breaking of the commandment can cost you eternal life.

Religious acts that you perform are unacceptable to me while between you and another person there lies a grievance.

Drop everything, go and set the matter right as far as lies within your power before you return to formal acts of worship.

For another illustration of the claims of the divine law I quoted the commandment, 'You shall not commit adultery.' The lust-look or lust-thought is enough to make you a fornicator in heaven's eyes. Be desperately determined to be pure — at all costs! Divorce — for any cause except unchastity — should in this same spirit be discountenanced.

Let the beauty of purity and dignity even extend to your speech, to the point where your honesty and sincerity are so evident that you will never have to bolster your 'yes' or your 'no' with oaths or vows.

The spirit of retaliation should not be found among you. Be disarmingly gracious and gentle to those who are nasty, not paying back in kind. Pay back in love, helpfulness and generosity.

'You have heard, "Love your neighbour, hate your enemy." But I say: Love your *enemies!* Pray for your *persecutors!* Only so can you be children of your heavenly Father. He makes his sun rise on good and bad alike. He sends rain on the just and the unjust. To love those who love you is no more than even scoundrels and heathen do!

'You must take your heavenly Father as your example in perfect goodness.'

THE FATHER'S WILL 26

We spent most of the day on the hill. I gave them only as much at a time as they could take in. We stretched our legs, at times scattered all over the hillside before returning, and in those intervals sick people were brought forward and healed.

Among the concepts which I stressed were the following:

Your 'light' must banish darkness — but take care not to make a show of your good deeds. You must be modest, your motives unselfish. The good that is done for self-glory is not accepted by the Father.

This modesty must include your prayers. Never pray to impress people. Nor try to impress God with your prayers — he knows your heart, and your words before you utter them. Separate yourself with God and speak with him alone, spontaneously instead of with set prayers or clichés, along these lines:

'Our Father in heaven, may your name be hallowed, may your kingdom come, may your will be done on earth as it is done in heaven. Care for all our needs today. Forgive us the wrong we have done, just as we have forgiven those who have wronged us. Keep us clear of temptation, and save us from all that is evil.'

Also, if you fast you must make sure that you are modest and spiritually minded. Do not call attention to yourself or the fasting. It is a matter between God and you.

You cannot serve God with a divided heart. Do not set your heart on temporary riches, but on eternal wealth.

To do this you need a true vision of life, a high purpose. Dedicate yourself to it. Compromise with nothing that taints, nothing that befogs your idealism.

Trust God implicitly. As you live for God, making his interests paramount to all others, he cares for you one day at a time. Look at the beauty of field and flower; an infinitely greater beauty, that of his own character, will he impart to your soul. You have a caring Father!

Do not think yourself better than others, and set yourself up as their judge. Love and good sense require rather that you be honestly self-critical.

When people are impervious to all spiritual reasoning, do not argue with them over sacred matters.

Humility, repentance, gentleness, self-control, full obedience to God's expressed will, mercy, purity, peace, a life that reflects the character of God, joy even under persecution, love, perfect goodness, modesty, unselfishness, a vital prayer life, single-mindedness towards God, a lofty vision, faith, good sense . . . do you feel overwhelmed by the graces required in my kingdom of grace? Ask, and it shall be given you! Whatever you need, whichever of these graces you lack — ask the Father! His help, blessing and gifts are yours for the asking!

Such love in your Father demands unselfish love in you — nothing less than that you treat others as you would like them to treat you. That is the underlying principle of the Law and the Prophets.

What I am spelling out to you is no easy way, but a hard and narrow road that can be reached only by a narrow gate entered by few. There *is* a broad road travelled by the many — but it leads to loss of life.

To escape this broad way, be on your guard against false religious teachers. They will impress you as harmless and guileless. Actually they are a potential disaster to you.

If they seem so innocent and sincere, how can you tell that they are people to avoid? By their fruits! Are they doing the will of my heavenly Father? They might zealously call me, 'Lord,' but they will never enter heaven unless they *do God's will*. In the day of reckoning many will say to me, 'Lord, Lord, didn't we preach in your name, didn't we cast out devils in your name, didn't we do great miracles in your name?' And I will have to tell them to their face, 'I have never known you. Go away, you who have worked on the side of evil!

'Everyone who hears these words of mine and puts them into practice is wise, like a man who builds his house on solid rock. When flood and storm swept against his house it never fell. But those who hear my instructions and fail to act on them are foolish. Their house, built on sand, will collapse with a mighty crash.'

We were going into Capernaum when a dignified group of Jewish elders from the synagogue came to meet us. Their usual attitude towards me was one of wary neutrality, but now they were handwringingly friendly.

'Sir, the captain of the local Roman army garrison needs help of a special kind. He's a wonderful man, most worthy of your help. He built the synagogue for us out of his own funds. A slave of his who means a great deal to him is desperately sick — in fact, he's dying in terrible pain and paralysis. He asked us to intercede with you. Won't you please go to his home and see if you can't heal the slave?'

I nodded and set off with them. We moved slowly, hemmed in on all sides by the crowd. Ahead, youngsters sprinted off to tell the captain that we were on our way.

Within minutes friends of his arrived and breathlessly fought their way through the press of people.

'Master!' they said, bowing. 'Our friend the captain sends his respects and says please don't put yourself out by coming to his home. If you would be kind enough just to say the word, he would be eternally grateful.'

A valuable lesson was developing for my disciples and the elders. The captain and I had never set eyes on each other. It was on the testimony of others that he was showing this faith. A man of pagan origins who had come to believe in the true God but was still trying to grope his way through considerable ignorance, was setting this example.

I acknowledged the message but continued on my way. Soon we were within sight of the captain's house and he himself, an unusually tall man of commanding presence, was coming through the crowd.

'Master,' he said earnestly, 'I felt unworthy to approach you personally. This is why I sent others. You really have no need to come to my home. This is too much of an honour for someone like me. Please just say the word, if you are willing, and I know my slave will be well.'

He knew about the Jewish official whose son I had healed at a distance. 'Do you want me to heal your slave from here?' I asked.

He spoke quietly, without excitement. 'Master, I wield authority. I give orders and men jump to obey. If you give the order, my servant's life will be saved.'

How I wished the 'believers' had such faith!

'Believe me,' I said to all listening, 'I have never seen faith like this, even in Israel! I tell you, many will come from all over the world to take their place in the kingdom of heaven with Abraham, Isaac and Jacob. And many who have belonged to the kingdom will be left to outer darkness, the place of tears and anguish.'

To the captain I said, 'Go home. Be it done for you as you have believed.' His eyes were moist. He knew what had just happened at his home; and when he and his friends got there a few minutes later they found the servant up and about with not a trace of sickness on him.

TWO BLIND MEN 28

On another occasion faith rose to meet divine power.

As my disciples and I were going down a street two blind men followed us, crying, 'Son of David, have pity on us!'

Yes, they believed in me as Son of David, the Messiah. I would heal them, but not here in the street. My main reasons for healing people were to reveal the Father's love and advance the kingdom of heaven in people's hearts. Unfortunately, these spiritual objectives were being lost sight of and an unhealthy excitement was springing up around the miracles.

I pressed on through the throng avid for another

miracle, and went into the house whose hospitality I was enjoying. Still pleading, the blind men were led in after me, as I knew they would be.

'Do you believe that I have the power to do what you are asking?'

'We do, Lord!'

I touched their sad, blank eyes. 'As you have believed, so be it.'

While those eyes surged full of light and they were too overwhelmed to speak, I said urgently and sternly, 'Take care not to spread this about.' And I sighed as they left, because I knew they would do just the opposite.

I was about to see faith of a different nature at work. As the two, now sighted, men rushed overjoyed from the house, a poor depraved creature in the power of a demon was led in.

'This man is dumb, Master,' one of those leading him said expectantly.

I spoke a word and the victim was at once a free man. He had not uttered a sound in years — now he was thanking God.

At that moment the religious leaders present turned away and left the room. Outside, the word was going like wildfire through the crowd, 'Nothing like this has ever been seen in Israel!'

'No!' said the religious leaders. 'You don't understand what is happening here. His power comes from Satan! It is by Satan's power that he casts out demons!'

And that was faith — faith in Satan, faith that Satan's power was allied to my message which saved men from disobedience, to a hunger and thirst to do God's will; and a limitless faith in their own powers of judgement. But towards their Messiah they barricaded their hearts.

Inside, the man wrested from Satan's grasp was kneeling at my feet.

We were going through Galilee for the second time, visiting as many towns and villages as possible, when we came to the village of Nain. The twelve were with me and able to see in action the principles and power of the heavenly kingdom. So were many others who trailed along, including some women who had been healed of demons or sickness — Mary Magdalene, who had had a sevenfold deliverance from Satan's power, Joanna, wife of Chuza who was King Herod's steward, and Susanna. These women were totally committed to our work and gave invaluable help.

Approaching Nain from the east along the steep and rocky road, we had passed the cemetery and were nearing the gate when a funeral train came through. Most of the villagers were in it, mourning and wailing along behind the open wickerwork coffin.

My eye fell on the widow, blind with tears, being led by friends behind the corpse of her only child and support, a young man. In her great love for her son she was devastated with grief, ashen-faced and hardly able to walk. It tore at my heart to see her condition, and I found myself choking.

Going quickly to her side, I said, 'Stop crying, dear Mother!' She was totally bewildered, trying to make out who I was.

As I touched the coffin the pallbearers halted and I looked down in the sudden silence at the boy in his linen shroud. The people crowded in on all sides, uttering my name. I was aware of intense activity as my adversary and his angels marshalled all their power to hold the corpse in the grip of death.

With a prayer to my Father, whose heart was touched just like mine over the widow's desolation, I said, 'Young man, get up!'

He opened his eyes. I helped him to sit up.

'Here is your son, Mother, alive and well,' I said. Sobbing and shaking, she took him in her arms, and I turned away with stinging eyes as friends began to unwind the shroud.

An awe akin to fear had fallen upon all, and they began to praise God, calling me a prophet and saying that God cares for his people — which is true.

The news of this would spread all over, even throughout Judea. The love of my Father's kingdom had been seen, and its power. And restoring to a young man some more years of mortality would, I hoped, serve to many men and women as a guarantee of the immortality which I offered to all.

THE SOWER 30

Later the same day I went down to the lakeside. Instead of crossing the lake in the waiting boat, I spoke to the expectant crowd which soon grew to such proportions that I had to teach from the boat. The most thought-provoking way to teach people about God's mysterious kingdom being by parables, I decided to use them extensively for the first time.

A farmer was sowing seed in the hillside. I pointed to him and said, 'A farmer was sowing grain in his fields. Some seed fell on a footpath, and the birds came and ate it up. Some fell on rocky ground where there was little soil, where it sprouted quickly, but lacking deep roots it soon withered in the sun. Other seeds fell among thorns, which flourished and choked out the tender blades. And some of the seed fell into good soil where it produced a crop — some a hundred times what had been sown, some sixty and some thirty times. If you have spiritual insight, understand this.'

Later, my disciples were to come and ask why I used parables in teaching the people, and I would reply, 'You have a ready perception for spiritual things that many find incomprehensible.' So they needed no special teaching techniques; or at any rate not to the same extent as most. 'Those with a keen spiritual desire will rapidly grow in knowledge until they can share with others. Those who neglect this capacity will lose even what they seemed to have, becoming blind with open eyes, dead with open ears, understanding nothing they hear. To help those weak in spiritual receptiveness, I speak to them in parables.'

The disciples had been guessing at the meaning of the parable of the sower, and they had been largely correct. I would explain it to them as follows: Some who hear about the kingdom of God have no spiritual understanding, no sense of their own dire need. The devil sees to it that the seed sown in their minds is soon snatched away. They are the footpath hearers.

The rocky-ground hearers are people of impulse and emotion, who happily accept the message. But it is a superficial experience, there is no change in the life, and it all evaporates when the going gets hard.

The thorny-ground hearers do a more thorough work with what they hear, but there is no moral transformation to weed out habits and tendencies and worldly aspirations that expose them to temptation and a barren experience.

The good-soil hearers make a full surrender to the Spirit of God, who enables them to bear fruit in various degrees of richness to the glory of God.

THE KINGDOM IS 31

From the boat I put another parable to the crowd: 'The kingdom of heaven is like this. A man sowed good seed in his field, but while his workmen slept his enemy came, sowed darnel among the wheat, and left. When the wheat grew, so did the weeds. The farmer's men came to him and said, "Sir, wasn't it good seed that you sowed in your field? Where have all the weeds come from?" He replied, "An enemy is responsible for this." The men said, "Shall we pull up the weeds?" "No," he replied, "you may pull up some wheat by mistake. Let both grow together until the harvest, when we shall have the reapers gather the weeds first and bind them in bundles to be burned, then gather the wheat for my barn.'

I am the heavenly farmer, sowing the good seed of saving truth in the world, my field. My adversary does his best to spoil my work by sowing bearded darnel, which is indistinguishable from wheat in its earlier stages. As with Judas Iscariot among the disciples, the wheat and the darnel grow together, both in the world and in the kingdom of grace. Some zealous workers want to treat the field with religious persecution to get rid of the darnel, but I have given no man any such work to do. In the harvest time which is the judgement at the time of the end, not human workmen but my angels will sort out the weeds for burning — the people who are not obedient to my Father's will. Then will the precious wheat, the righteous doers of God's will, receive their glorious reward . . .

Another parable: 'The kingdom of heaven is like a mustard seed, which a man took and planted in his field. It is smaller than any other of your seeds, but grows bigger than any other garden plant, a tree for birds to nest in.'

The scoffers looked on my work as insignificant, but from small beginnings it would grow and reach out to the ends of the earth.

'The kingdom of heaven is like yeast which a woman took and mixed into her flour, and it activated the whole lump of dough.'

My teachings would quietly, invisibly work in the life of my true follower, transforming the whole of it.

'The kingdom of heaven is like treasure buried in a field. The man who found it covered it over again, and delightedly sold all he possessed to buy that field.'

So great is the value of the salvation treasure hidden in the field of Scripture, that it is worth all you can muster to unearth and possess it.

'And the kingdom of heaven is like a merchant looking

for fine pearls. He discovered one of such rare value that he sold all he had and bought it.'

This pearl is the one King Solomon called 'the chiefest of ten thousand', whom to know is life eternal. Neither he nor his salvation can be bought; yet they cost everything you have.

To emphasize graphically that my parables were meant to be understood, I reminded them that a lighted lamp is not brought into a dark room only to be placed under a bucket or under a bed. Its place is on the lamp stand. What seems 'hidden' is meant to come to light, be disclosed; prick up your ears and understand!

STORM ON THE LAKE 32

The sermon by the lake ended, we prepared to cross to the other side.

Aware of the faintness of hunger, I lay down in the stern of the boat, pulled a covering of oiled skins over me and fell into a sleep of exhaustion.

We must have been about halfway across the lake of Galilee, crowded by the accompanying boats, everything placid and quiet but for the creak and lisp of oars, when the wind came up. Within a minute or two a squall was blowing, shipping up great waves that flung the boats like chips of wood.

There were great thunder claps and jagged flashes of lightning. The boats began to ship water and the crews bailed and battled to face the storm. Through it all I slept.

Waves were coming over the side and the bailing was having little effect. My disciples saw that we were going down. In panic they cried, 'Master! Master!' but their voices were caught away by the storm. In sloshing water they held on to one another, blind in the darkness, and shrieked out my name. There was no response, and doubt assailed them.

Had I been snatched away? Had they been abandoned to face death?

A flash of lightning showed me in the stern, lost to the turmoil and the danger. Two men groped their way to me and shook me hard. I sat up, aware of water in my face and a shriek of wind in my ears. One put his lips to my ear.

'Lord! We're sinking! Don't you care if we drown?'

Another flash. They took my peaceful expression for unconcern.

'Lord, save us! We're dying!'

I shook the cover from my shoulders and stood up, lifting my hand. At that moment a great lightning flash showed some other boats, also in desperate trouble, people staring our way.

'Quiet! Be still!'

The thunder rolled back, there was a long foam-bubble hissing, and the howling storm was gone. Our ears tingled with the sudden silence, the boat rode over a wave or two and then it was just a gentle swell. The heavy clouds had parted and the stars shone through, moonlight spilled over us.

I saw the other boats with crouching staring people. My disciples had subsided in a heap and their eyes were wide animals' eyes.

'Why are you overcome with terror?' I asked sadly. 'Do you still have no faith? Oh, you of little faith . . . '

There was a stir among them and I heard whispers of 'What kind of man is this? Even the wind and the waves obey him!'

They had forgotten my words of that day in Jerusalem when I was challenged because I had cured the paralysed man at Bethesda. I had said, 'I assure you, the Son does *nothing* of his own accord.'

This was the Father's power. It was a love-power just as available to them as to the one at whom they were gaping, to save them not only from storm and crashing wave but particularly from the raging passions of temptation.

With the pearly iridescence of first light on the lake, we stepped out on the eastern shore where lived the Gerasenes. The boats were beached and we made our way up the slope. I had come seeking a few hours' rest from the crowd, time to eat and pray; but part of the previous day's audience had come along.

Suddenly a raw shriek cut through the air. We saw a hairy, naked man bounding towards us from a cemetery, bellowing insanely and waving arms from which swung lengths of broken chain. Behind him came another, less noisy but no less menacing. All those with me fled screaming.

The depraved madmen, demon-possessed, lived among the tombs and were so violent that no one ventured down this road. They had broken the chains which had once briefly subdued them, and were a mass of scars and sores from cutting themselves with sharp stones.

They came at me, glaring, foaming at the mouth, lips drawn back from their teeth, bloodthirsty. My heart went out to them.

When they were a few paces away I raised my hand. Their headlong rush was broken and they came to a lurching stop, raging, grinding their teeth.

While I stood pondering the men's bloodshot eyes, tormented faces and self-inflicted wounds, my disciples plucked up courage and trickled back to stand behind me.

'You evil spirit, come out . . . ' I began.

A sound of hope, of deliverance, broke through to those darkened minds. They dropped to their knees to plead for help. Instead of the cry for help there came a rush of angry words from one of the men. 'What do you want with me, Jesus, Son of the Most High God? In God's name don't torment me!'

So that my disciples could gain an insight into what

they would have to contend with, I asked, 'What is your name?'

'My name is Legion! We are many!'

There had not been many angels of Satan earlier, I knew — my adversary was not one to waste spirit-power. So totally were the men in his power that one angel could control both of them, often even at a distance. But my adversary had failed in his effort to drown me in the storm, and had brought in reinforcements for the murderous attempt on my life on shore.

The two men in the spirits' power writhed in a vain effort to call for divine intervention. A great deal of spirit activity was going on. The spirits, surrounded by my Father's angels, were desperate because of their double failure; but even in their desperation they lost none of their craftiness. Once more I was face to face with my old adversary and all his forces.

'Look, those pigs there on the hillside!' they cried. 'Will you allow us to exchange control of these humans for control over them?'

I saw what they planned to do. They would destroy the swine, and I would get the blame and be rejected by the Gerasenes.

That was as far as they could see. I could see further. My apparent defeat would lead to a greater victory than I had time to work for today.

'Go!' I said.

The two men collapsed, and the next moment there was a screeching and snorting among the two thousand or so swine and they began a mad stampede down the steep bluff to the narrow beach below. As those in front saw the water ahead they tried to stop or swing away, but the headlong pace carried them squealing into the lake where most of the swine soon drowned in the welter of panic.

While the swineherds fled to their employers with their tale, and my disciples struggled with the help of tools from the boats to get the manacles and fetters off, I had about an hour to talk to the men freed from demons. I gave them the basic message of my kingdom; they would soon need it.

Then hundreds of the Gerasenes descended upon us, wide-eyed with horror over the destruction of wealth. Ignoring the two erstwhile maniacs of whom they had formerly gone in fear of their lives, who now sat neatly clothed and in their right mind at my feet, they pleaded that I leave their country.

Never one to force myself on others, I went to the boat. There the two liberated men begged to come along.

'You must go home,' I said. 'Tell your friends what God has done for you.'

As the boats pulled away from the shore, Judas Iscariot was shaking his head. I knew what he was thinking. Has there ever been a pair of missionaries more pathetically unprepared, more unpromising than those two scarred, matted-haired men on the shore! The only visible asset they had was the clothing donated by my disciples. And why did the Master allow the swine to be destroyed? After all, they were worth money, a great deal of money!

I'd leave him and the others guessing until we returned to these shores in ten months' time.

JAIRUS'S DAUGHTER 34

Jairus, president of the synagogue, had used his authority to get through the throng outside and now appeared in the doorway. He was distraught, flinging himself to his knees at my feet.

'Please, sir, come to my home at once! My little daughter is at death's door! I beg you to come and lay your hands on her. Come, make her well, save her life!'

Astounding behaviour, considering who he was and the presence of witnesses from the Sanhedrin.

Outside we found the street choked with people who had to be carried along with us if we were to make any progress at all. We moved at a snail's pace, Jairus sweating profusely with anxiety and pleading with the people to move out of the way. But I knew we were about to be held up.

A woman was trying feebly but desperately to reach me. She had heard of the healings. For twelve years she had been subject to bleeding, had dragged herself through her days. Earlier today she had tried in vain to get through the crowd that welcomed me to Capernaum. Now she was panting with weakness, almost sobbing, again unable to reach me. I stopped to give her a better chance. She was almost doubled up, reaching forward, her eyes on my robe . . . 'If only I can but touch his clothes, I'll be cured!' she thought; and then her fingers were on the seam.

As the energy flowed through her, she knew that she was cured. She straightened up, overwhelmed with joy, light-headed with a flood of gratitude.

'Who touched me?' I asked.

Peter looked at me in surprise. 'Everyone is touching you, Lord, jostling you. What do you mean, "Who touched me"?'

With my eyes on her I said, 'Someone touched my clothes. I felt the flow of healing power.'

Tremblingly she cringed closer and went down on her knees. Through her tears she poured out the story of her twelve years of suffering and of the healing just experienced.

Because I abhor superstition it had to be made clear that my clothes held no magical power, that her touch was incidental.

'My daughter,' I said to her, loudly enough so that many could get the lesson, 'your *faith* has made you well! Go in peace, and remain well.'

It had been my Father's will to heal her. His angels had brought her to me, his Spirit had prompted her to faith; but at any stage she could have doubted, turned away. And now she had testified to what God had done for her, thereby strengthening her own soul. With a happiness matching her own joy, I turned back to Jairus.

'Please hurry, sir,' he said hoarsely. 'She seemed to be dying!'

'What is her age?'

'She is 12, sir.'

His hand was shaking on my arm. We set off once more, but I knew that his daughter was dead.

Minutes later men were ploughing their way through the crowd. Wide-eyed with tension, one of them put his mouth to Jairus's ear.

'It's no use bothering the master any further,' I heard him say. 'I'm sorry. Your daughter is dead.'

Jairus gave a shuddering, despairing cry.

'No!' I said to him. 'Don't be afraid. Only have faith.'

Before we reached the house we could hear the flute players and the wailing of the mourners, which jarred on me.

'Why all this noise and weeping?' I asked. 'The child is not dead but asleep.'

The mourners poured scorn on my words. They had tested the child for breathing and heartbeat.

'Get them all out of here,' I said to Jairus.

It was a small room. I took only the parents and Peter, James and John, and shut out the noise.

She was thin, underweight. I took the tiny hand in mine and in the presence of the Spirit and God's angels said, 'Get up, my child.'

As her heart began to beat, a tremor passed through her. Her eyes opened, found her parents, and she smiled and sat up.

I gave the sobbing parents a few minutes with her, then said, 'Do give her something to eat, will you? And please say as little as you can about this matter.'

I had faithful John the Baptist on my mind every day. Life was hard for him in the dungeon. He had nothing to fall back on but his own spiritual resources.

His disciples brought him news that had reached them of the dead son of the widow of Nain, whom I came across as he was being carried to the cemetery.

'If he can bring a day-old corpse back to life by speaking a word, why doesn't he free you from this dark hole, Master?' they wanted to know.

John was at a loss for a reply. 'After all, you were his forerunner, his right hand. If he can free a man from the bonds of death — from death! — why doesn't he speak a simple word to get his main apostle out of prison?'

My adversary was overjoyed at their words. Well-meaning friends can bring the keenest torment to a sufferer's soul; in fact, they can more easily drive him to despair than a declared enemy.

'And why doesn't he take the throne of King David and drive out the Romans? Isn't this what the Messiah is to do, as everyone knows? Why, even our enemies know it — the Sanhedrin, the Pharisees and Sadducees! Instead, he's spending all his time recruiting disciples for himself. And fraternizing with backward people and despised classes.'

Their doubts plunged John into an agony of incomprehension. At the same time, self-doubt was nagging at him. He had been bitterly disappointed at the results of his mission. He thought he was launching a great work of revival and reformation, moving the nation towards God in repentance. And where had it led to? Even his own disciples doubted the Messiahship of the one whom he had pointed out as the 'Sent of God'!

Where had he gone wrong? What had he done wrong, or failed to do? Where had his hold on God's wisdom and guidance faltered? Had he been abandoned behind these dark walls for the past six months because he had failed God?

Naggingly the disciples urged the question on him, 'Is he really the Messiah, Master? Or should we expect someone else?'

'Why don't you go and put that question to him?' he asked quietly. 'Then come and tell me what he says.' *He hoped they would become as unshakeable as he on this point,* and would also bring information on the things he could not understand.

The two chosen messengers walked up and across the Jordan valley for three days to Galilee, and found me surrounded by a throng of people. They worked their way through, introduced themselves as John's disciples, and put the question, 'Our master sent us to ask, "Are you the one who was to come, or should we expect someone else?" '

There was a ripple of shock among those who heard. Had John the Baptist lost confidence? Was he looking elsewhere? If John no longer believed . . .

'Will you be setting off on your return journey tomorrow morning?' I asked.

'That was our plan, Master.'

'Then you wouldn't mind waiting till this evening for my answer.'

The sick were coming in a seemingly endless stream. Blind people were groping their way forward, or being led. A touch or a word, and they could see, some for the first time in their lives. The deaf left with normal hearing. People in a feverish coma stood to their feet, cured. Paralysed people came on stretchers, and walked away with their stretchers under their arms. Terminally sick people who had reached the end, demon-possessed people, people full of a deadly infection, even lepers — all were made well by the power of God through the ministry of the angels who attended me.

After this, John's men saw me gather the poor and

illiterate outcasts and speak to them the words of eternal life.

At last the tiring but satisfying day was over and I motioned John's men closer.

'Go and tell John what you have seen and heard. The blind receive their sight, the paralysed walk, lepers are cleansed, the deaf hear, the dead are raised to life. And people shunned by the religious leaders have the good news of God's kingdom preached to them. When you have told John all this, tell him, "Blessed is the man who does not find me a stumbling block." '

When John's messengers had left, I swept the crowd with a glance.

'What was the sight that drew you to the wilderness? A reed swayed by the wind?' No — the expediency-first men of religion, who swayed so easily to the winds of popular opinion and coercion, were not in the wilderness but here.

'If not, what did you go out to see? A man in imposing attire? Hardly — such people live in palaces. Why then did you go out? To see a prophet? Decidedly, and much more than a prophet! This is the one about whom it is written, "I will send my messenger, and he shall prepare the way before me." In view of this I tell you: never has mankind produced a greater man than John the Baptist! Yet . . . the one who is least in the kingdom of heaven is greater than he.'

No Moses or Abraham was greater in moral worth, or as exalted in being as the personal herald of the long-awaited Messiah; yet in comparison with John's dungeon existence the humblest convert to the kingdom of heaven who is privileged to be in the Messiah's presence daily, like yourselves, is more highly honoured.

'All the people who heard John, even the tax collectors, acknowledged God's righteousness by undergoing John's baptism, but the Pharisees and theologians rejected purpose of God for themselves by not undergoing his baptism.

'Ever since the coming of John the Baptist, the concept of the kingdom of heaven has forged ahead, forceful people laying hold of it. John's work was climactic, all the prophets and the Law having prophesied with John's day in mind. If you can accept it, John is the "Elijah" who was to come. If you have understanding, understand that!

'To what can I compare this generation? They are like children sitting in the market-place and shouting at each other, "You're not playing the game by my rules!" John came with an abstemious, even austere, way of living — so they said the devil had got into him. The Son of Man came without so much fasting and asceticism, so they were ready with the distortion, "Here is a glutton and a drunkard, a friend of tax collectors and sinners!" Let wisdom by judged by its consistency!'

Everything I do is misrepresented by my accusers. The only reason why I associate with 'sinners' (the 'righteous' are sinners too, so it is really only a matter of degree) is to influence them for heaven.

To make my point, I exclaimed concerning towns well represented among my audience, 'Woe to you, Chorazin! Woe to you, Bethsaida! If the miracles performed in you had been performed in Tyre and Sidon, they would have repented long ago in sackcloth and ashes. I assure you, it will be more bearable for Tyre and Sidon in the day of judgement than for you.

'And as for you, Capernaum, will you be exalted to heaven? No, you will be brought low, to the grave. If Sodom had seen the miracles that you have seen, Sodom would be standing today. I assure you, it will be more bearable for the land of Sodom in the day of judgement than for you.'

But my Father always has his 'remnant' of faithful ones, who are usually not renowned for their learning or in other ways prominent — 'little children' in the opinion of the wise and influential.

'O Father, Lord of heaven and earth, I thank you for

"hiding" these things from the wise and learned, but revealing them to little children. Yes, I thank you, Father, that you delight in such graciousness.'

My eye went down the ages to the time of the judgement. I saw seething masses of people, an endless procession from cradle to grave. Every one was loved by the Father. Some chose to live without their Maker's help or blessing. How hard their life was — empty, devoid of permanency, a death-march. Others tried to serve the Creator, but in ways conceived by man, not God: pilgrimages, penances, a hollow round of prayer, works of salvation and merit, charms, superstition — all dreary and sad. Yet others were slaves to passions that shattered their peace, split their personalities. For them all I had a fervent and tender message.

'Come to me, all you who are exhausted, overburdened! Bend your necks to *my* yoke, learn from *me*. I am gentle and humble-hearted. Under my yoke, which is easy and light, you will find rest for your souls.'

SHEEP AMONG WOLVES

36

Her eyes were harassed, the lines between them unerasable even by a smile. It was early in the day, but she already looked tired, careworn. My glance went to the others. The whole crowd had a quality of lostness about it, like a flock of sheep without a shepherd.

All through the land it was like this — men and women going huddled under the cares of life, the sorrows of disease and death. My heart went out to them in a pity so great that I felt it could tear me apart.

Calling my disciples to me, I said, 'The harvest is great but the workers few. Pray to the Lord of the harvest, to send out workers into his harvest field.'

They did so, one at a time, and I listened to their prayers. Twelve simple, brief prayers, but by the time they had finished I knew that they sensed something of the great need, and were ready to answer the prayers by offering themselves.

'The Lord of the harvest is sending out the twelve of you,' I said. 'Listen carefully to your instructions. The burden of your preaching must be, "The kingdom of heaven is at hand." Heal the sick, raise the dead, cleanse lepers, cast out devils. You have received free of charge; give free of charge.

'Take along no money, no travel bag, no change of clothes or extra sandals or staff — the worker is worth his keep. When you get to a town or village, find out who in it is highly regarded and stay with him until you leave. Wish the house peace as you enter it. If the family deserve it, the peace of your blessing will come to them; if they do not, they will forfeit it. If you are refused a welcome or a hearing, when you have left that house or town shake the dust of it from your feet.

'I am sending you out like sheep among wolves. Be alert as serpents, innocent as doves. Be on your guard against people. They will persecute you, and torture you in their places of worship. On my account you will be brought before rulers and kings . . . .'

I gave the twelve authority to cast out demon spirits and to cure every kind of ailment and disease, then sent them out in pairs. Peter went with Andrew, James with John, Philip with Nathanael, Thomas with Matthew, James of Alphaeus with Judas, and fiery Simon with Judas Iscariot the schemer. They had to stretch their wings on their own, yet aided by my angels and the Spirit.

'Nobody should be called by my name who does not take up his cross and walk in my footsteps,' I had said to the twelve. That 'cross' is daily putting God first in the life, and doing so without flinching before the pressures brought to bear by others.

The cross I would be carrying to my own crucifixion

was often in my mind, and it was a symbol to me of the daily battle against prejudice, abuse, and half-heartedness in those who accepted me; and persecution by the church leaders.

THE FORERUNNER'S END

37

While the twelve were busy with their missionary tour, I set off with other disciples to preach the kingdom of God in the towns of Galilee. In due course I came to Nazareth, my own place, visited my mother, brothers, sisters and friends, healed a few people and was again allowed to teach in the synagogue. The result was disappointing.

'Where does he get this wisdom from?' the people cavilled. 'How does he work such miracles? We can't deny the wisdom and miracles, but what's the source of it? We know Mary his mother, his brothers James, Joseph, Judas and Simon, and his sisters. We know him — he's after all only a carpenter who grew up among us!'

The town buzzed with my name; but I did not fit their idea of a world conqueror and they rejected me. In other places crowds of sick people came or were brought on stretchers. Because of the unbelief in my Messiahship here, few came. And because few presented themselves, I did very little healing in Nazareth — nothing that the people would have regarded as a spectacular miracle. Elsewhere I had left entire villages without a moan of sickness in any house. In Nazareth all who came were healed, but considerable sickness remained when I left . . . left never to return.

A few days later John the Baptist's disciples appeared among my audience. A glance at their faces was enough to tell me what news they had brought.

John the Baptist had been imprisoned for telling King Herod Antipas that it was wrong for him to have taken his brother's wife Herodias. With vengeance in her heart, the woman waited until the king celebrated his birthday with a lavish party, and had her daughter Salome dance for him. Dazed with drink, he grandly offered to reward the girl in any way she wished. Prompted by her fiendish mother, she asked for John's head on a dish. The decadent Herod was horror-stricken, and would have spared the prophet's life if just one of his nobles or officers had spoken a word on behalf of the godly man, but alcohol had robbed them of humanity and decency.

'And you have buried John?' I asked.

'Yes, Master.' John's disciples looked at me, eyes full of unexpressed emotions.

'You are wondering why I never visited John, or worked a miracle to release him from prison,' I said.

Later I took them for a walk and explained. 'John was not forsaken, not alone in his dungeon. The Father's angels never left his side, and they helped him to have a very precious experience in the Scriptures. John was conscious of God's presence. Didn't you see his confidence, his strength?'

They acknowledged that John had been remarkably strong, had seemed to grow even more so towards the end.

'John was the forerunner of my mission, forerunner of the Messiah. He never weakened in that work and that faith, did he?'

'Never, Master.' Their eyes wavered before mine. Their expressions of doubt had been a trial to John. He had allowed them to bring a question of uncertainty to me — but the question had been theirs, not John's, and John had only permitted it in order to establish their confidence.

'Now listen to this. He was my forerunner in something else as well — abuse, suffering, death. No greater privilege can come to a man or woman. And know this — many, many in years to come must, like John, drink the cup of martyrdom. They will derive great strength from the example of John, the one loved by God and highly lauded by the Son of Man, who was allowed to bear his witness to history as a believer who was apparently — but not actually — deserted . . . yet died absolutely faithful.'

I added, 'John died victorious, and is for ever beyond the power of temptation. He sleeps in God for a while. Are you, as disciples of John, going to be as full of faith?'

FOOD FOR THE MASSES

38

So powerfully was Galilee roused by my work, as well as by that of my disciples as they witnessed in pairs from place to place, that King Herod trembled and expressed the fear that John the Baptist had risen from the dead and was performing all these miracles.

The day arrived when my disciples and I were to come together once more, and they found me surrounded by thousands of people outside Capernaum. They were thrilled and happy, I could see, but as tired as I was from the ceaseless activity. They had been performing miracles, as had I, but it would be unthinkable to work a miracle to banish our fatigue.

'Come with me, just you yourselves' — and I included John's disciples — 'to some out-of-the-way place where you can rest undisturbed.'

We set out across the lake of Galilee, leaving the huge crowd, out since earliest dawn, to go home for breakfast. On the eastern shore we found a deserted hill. With great relief we relaxed over a very late simple breakfast. The men reported on their efforts and I pointed out how they could improve, then opened to them more fully the treasures of divine truth. We had time for prayer and were feeling much refreshed when the same crowd as earlier descended upon us. They had made their way all round the northern shore of the lake on foot!

There were thousands of them, and as I saw them

gathering I turned deliberately to slow-to-believe Philip and said, 'These dear eager souls did not, after all, go home for something to eat. They'll be with us all day. How can we buy food for them?'

He stared at them, at a loss for a reply.

I welcomed the people and taught them while they crowded in so solidly that there was no room to get them seated on the grass. Hours later mothers were still standing with babies on their hips or in their arms, weary but attentive. Just after mid-afternoon there was a respite and I looked at Philip.

He shrugged. 'I've worked it out, Lord. If I hired myself out for two hundred days my total earnings would hardly supply these people with a bite to eat. There are about five thousand men, besides women and children. It's impossible! We'll have to send them away to go and buy something for themselves in the villages.'

'They do not need to go away,' I said. 'You give them something to eat.'

Andrew said, 'Lord, since you spoke to Philip this morning I've been looking around. There's a boy here with five small barley loaves and two small dried fish. But how far would that go in a crowd like this?' He smiled and shook his head.

'Have the people seated in orderly groups of about fifty,' I told them.

Staring, they hesitated for a moment before obeying. When the people had spread out more and were seated on the lush early-spring grass, Andrew brought the hand basket with the typical poor man's lunch.

'We need another eleven baskets,' I said. They found them, empty ones, as I knew they would.

Taking the small loaves in my hands, I blessed them and gave thanks to my Father for providing us with an abundance of food. Breaking the loaves into portions I filled the twelve baskets in an almost tangible silence, while not an eye blinked and not a breath seemed to be taken.

The disciples came back again and again for bread and fish until all had satisfied their hunger on that which the heavenly Father had provided in his love.

'Let none of God's generosity be abused through waste,' I said. 'Gather up all uneaten portions, so that nothing is lost.'

They filled twelve baskets with uneaten food. A lesson for you, I thought, of dependence upon God. Of his infinite resources. Of his tender care. Of his blessing on the simple rather than the luxurious. Of his use of disciples in the distribution of heaven's blessing.

WALKING ON THE LAKE 39

The people were clamouring for the twelve baskets of food, to take home and share with their friends; and I hoped they would share more than material bread.

The word began to go round in the crowd, 'This is indeed the Prophet who was to come to the world!' Here was one whom the crowds followed, who could lead the nation in a war against Rome. On the battlefield he could work miracles to heal all our wounded! He could keep our armies supplied with miracle food! At last Israel could be avenged on the Romans!

My disciples, in a glow of exultation, were flitting about among the people handing out souvenirs of bread and saying, 'Of course you're right. He is the Deliverer! . . . No, he's too modest to proclaim himself King. There'd have to be a popular movement to make him King by force . . . This is the right time, just before Passover!' Among the twelve, Judas Iscariot was foremost in this work, with Peter close on his heels.

I called my disciples urgently to my side.

'Take John's disciples, go to the boat at once! I'll dismiss the crowd and meet you just south of Capernaum. Cross the lake — now!'

'But, Lord!' They were incredulous, dismayed.

'Just go! I'll meet you on the other side.' They wandered down to the boat, dragging their heels.

The sun was setting. Everywhere the crowd was on its feet, surging forward to take me by force and proclaim me King. Men among them with a strong instinct for leadership were raising the cry, 'Israel's Deliverer! The throne of David revived!'

I raised my hand commandingly. The human tide was arrested.

'Dear people, you have had a full day,' I said. 'The kingdom of heaven has come close to you. Let us not try to change the kingdom of heaven into an earthly kingdom! You have seen the love of the Father. Hold on to that, as you return to your homes with the Father's blessing.'

I went up into a hill to pray. Down below, my disciples had not obeyed by setting out at once for the western shore. They were waiting, hoping I would not let this 'opportunity' slip through my fingers. Some of the crowd remained, milling about, still intent on crowning me King of Israel.

For hours I pleaded with the Father, not for myself but for power to reveal to people that my mission was divine and not earthly, so that with a pure understanding of this they might be immune to Satan's perversions of truth. And I prayed for my disciples. They would soon see my true coronation — a cross, not a throne. Their dreams of glory shattered, they would be exposed to powerful temptations. They would all fall away, never to recover their faith, unless the Spirit strengthened them and gave them understanding.

While I prayed for them under the twinkling stars, they were still on the shore below, unhappy with me. 'We were on the verge of a breakthrough!' Judas Iscariot kept saying. Peter said, 'After that amazing miracle we had them in our hands. For the first time we had a mass miracle, one experienced by everybody at the same time! We could have brought in the kingdom in no time at all!' They were in varying degrees exasperated at my actions.

My heart was heavy as they eventually shipped their oars and set off. At just about the time when they would have landed on the western shore had they obeyed my instructions, a storm blew up and threatened their boat. The intention behind the storm was to blot out those whom I was preparing to be part of the very foundation of my church; but my Father was overruling events for their good.

I had already set off as fast as I could walk, round the northern bight of the lake. My eye was on that storm-tossed boat all through the dark night. Those strong men strained at their oars, their stormy thoughts about me now over-whelmed by fear. They were fighting for their lives.

It was close to daybreak when, utterly exhausted, they gave up all efforts to save themselves, and cried to God for help. Blown far off course, they were reasonably close to shore without knowing it. I set out walking across the waves to meet them.

In the glow of light shed all about me by the angels, they saw me. Taking me for a ghost, they screamed in terror. My words cut through the storm, 'Take courage! It is I! Don't be afraid!'

They recognized me. Prompting them to faith, I made as if to pass them, and they cried out in an agony of despair for my help. At once I turned to them.

Peter, dear impossible, impulsive man, was ecstatic with joy. 'Lord, tell me to come to you on the water!'

It had been no part of my plan that he should do anything of this nature, but I said, 'Come!'

He came, borne up by my angels, eyes fixed on me, step after step just as I was doing. Then he thought of his friends behind him, and turned to see what impression he was making on them. With eyes off me, he sank. A wave went over him, raising the battered boat high. Strong swimmer that he was, Peter came up gasping, just in time to see another wave towering over him.

'Lord, save me!' he shrieked, and I had him by the hand, lifted him, and we walked hand in hand to the boat and stepped in.

At once the storm lost its power, the waves began to settle, and a gleam of moonlight showed the silvery strip of beach not far off.

They were all on their knees at my feet, worshipping, Peter totally subdued and silent. I accepted their worship. It was the first time they had confessed my divine sonship; and it had taken a close encounter with death to bring this about.

LIVING BREAD 40

In just one year the crisis would come: my betrayal, arrest, execution. It would come like a bolt from the blue, with devastating impact. My disciples had just worshipped at my feet, but their faith, such as it was, would be shattered. They had given up much to follow me — but not their pet preconceptions of a Messiah. That was why they were so eager to lead the crowd yesterday in proclaiming me King. Real spiritual thinking was still alien to them — they would collapse under the weight of my cross.

How, in divine love and wisdom, could I prepare them for the looming crisis?

So far, my words had not shaken them out of their complacency. 'The kingdom of heaven is — humility, sensing your need of God, heart-felt repentance, hungering and thirsting to obey God's will, compassion, purity, gladly suffering for God's sake . . . ' They had heard the words, nodded earnestly . . . and failed to make them their life and soul.

In Matthew's home I had predicted, 'The time will

come when the bridegroom will be forcibly removed from his friends.' They had not understood, nor bothered me for an explanation. They were building on sand and would be swept away in the coming flood.

The thousands who now dogged my steps were even shallower in motive. I was their celebrity; to hero-worship me was popular. I could heal them, feed them, soon annihilate the Romans for them. Materialism was their 'kingdom of heaven'.

Most insidiously dangerous was the fact that my core of true believers built their hopes on the crowds. The popularity went to their heads, warped their understanding of Scripture, blinded them to their need for a life and a character that conform to God's. It was only a question of time, they felt, and I'd yield to the acclaim of the masses and allow myself to be crowned.

In divine love and wisdom, the plan to strengthen my true followers against the crisis of Golgotha was launched yesterday, when the crowd was miraculously fed. The food was multiplied in compassion, in the love of the Father — but another reason also lay behind it. The end result of the miracle of love was foreseen: a crisis of faith. There would be an attempt to sweep me off my feet to high honour — followed by rejection when I refused.

The rejection would be today. To prepare my disciples for it, I had strengthened their faith by walking on the water and calming the raging storm. Today's crisis would strengthen them for the great one ahead. They would see my popularity vanish within minutes, and this would remove a temptation which they had neither the strength nor the desire to resist. All through the mortification about to come, I would be with them, helping them through. Only one of the true core of believers would be lost in the crisis of my crucifixion.

Soon after daybreak great numbers of people flocked to Bethsaida. Unable to find me, many of them came by boat and on foot to Capernaum, where they discovered me teaching in the synagogue. At sight of them my disciples were roused to new hopes of a coronation and spread the word about the storm on the lake and my walking on the water and calming the elements. The people, agog with excitement, surged about me, atitter with questions and set in their determination to get my co-operation today.

'Rabbi, how did you get here, when did you get here?' they gushed, ready to ooh and aah as I repeated the story they had heard from Judas, Peter and the rest.

'What are your motives in flocking after me?' I asked gently. The time had come to go to the heart of the matter. 'It is not that my words and miracles convinced you of my Messiahship, is it? Isn't it because I fed you, and you have further expectations of me on the earthly level?'

They were abashed, but still full of their plans for today.

'Do not preoccupy yourselves with food whose effect is temporary, but with the food of eternal life! This food is what the Son of Man would rather give you. On him God the Father has placed his authority.'

Uncomfortable with my words, they asked, 'What should we be doing if we are to satisfy God?'

Rabbis and theologians had joined them. Solemnly I replied, 'What God requires is that you *believe* in the one whom he has sent.'

There was silence, then a leader among them shouted, 'What miraculous sign can you give us, so that we can believe you?'

'Yes, what proof do you offer?' challenged another, and the crowd chorused their agreement with these sentiments.

I looked at my apostles and the other close disciples. They could not believe their ears. These very people demanding a miracle had eaten the miracle food only hours ago, and seen any number of healings!

'That's right! Our forefathers were given proof that

Moses was from God. He didn't merely multiply loaves of bread for them, he kept giving them manna, bread from heaven!'

'It was not Moses who gave them bread, but my Father in heaven — the same one who is now offering you the true bread from heaven.'

'That's what we want! Let's have this bread from now on!'

'The bread from God is he who comes down from heaven, the very one who is prepared to give life to the world. *I am that bread of life!*'

How I longed to put my arms about them! I was ready to give my life for them, and would soon do so. If only, instead of wanting to crown me as King of Israel, they would crown God as King of their hearts!

The rabbis and theologians showed shock at my claim to have come from heaven as 'the bread of life', and were starting to mutter indignantly.

I pleaded, 'He who comes to me will never go hungry, he who *believes* in me will never be thirsty. As far as you are concerned' — I looked at the religious leaders — 'I have already said that you have been subjecting me to scrutiny without *faith*. All moved upon by the Father — and responding to that moving — will come to me. I will drive no such person away, for I have come from heaven to do the will of him who sent me. He does not want me to lose even one who has responded to his call, but to see that soul safely through to the resurrection of eternal life at the last day. My Father wants everyone who contemplates the Son and *puts his faith in him* to live forever; and I myself will raise him up on the last day.'

While I spoke, my ceremonialist enemies had been quietly spreading their mutterings: 'How can he say he has come from heaven? He is Jesus son of Joseph — we know his parents!'

I would not defend myself by explaining the divine-human birth by which I entered this world. They had no hope of coming to any true understanding while they cherished a vicious spirit of fault-finding, which could only close their minds to the Father's guidance.

'Cease cavilling. No one is open to conviction about me unless the Father who sent me draws him. Those who open their minds to the Father are the ones whom I will raise up at the last day. It is written in the Prophets, "They will all be taught by God." Everyone who listens to the Father and heeds what he says, comes to me, the only one who has seen the Father. I tell you the truth, he who *believes* has everlasting life.'

To their reluctant question, 'How are we to satisfy God?' my reply had been *believe, have faith*. 'My Father wants everyone who contemplates the Son and *puts his faith in him* to live forever.' In one way or another I had said this five times. They were unconvinced.

My audience was exuberantly happy with me while I healed them or fed them miraculous food; but in the realm of spiritual living I was losing them. In heaven's wisdom people of darkened mind could best be reached by symbolic language.

'Your forefathers ate the manna in the desert, yet it did not keep them from dying. What I am offering you is the bread which has come down from heaven. If anyone eats this bread he shall live forever. This bread is my flesh! I will give it for the life of the world.'

A storm of dissent erupted among them, especially among the religious leaders. 'His flesh? How can this man give us his flesh to eat?'

I said, 'I assure you, unless you eat the flesh of the Son of Man and drink his blood, you can have no life in you. Whoever eats my flesh and drinks my blood possesses eternal life, and I will resurrect him at the last day. For my flesh is real food, my blood is real drink. Whoever eats my flesh and drinks my blood *shares my life* and I share his. Just as the living Father sent me and I am alive because of my union with the Father, so the one who feeds on me will live because of his union with me.

'This is the bread which came down from heaven. Our forefathers ate manna and died. He who feeds on this bread will live for ever.'

The religious leaders were heckling me while I talked. They now exploded, 'Outrageous! Cannibalism! Who's got time to spend listening to such talk?'

'Does this shock you? How much more shocked you would be if you saw the Son of Man ascending to where he was before! Listen to this: It is spiritual food that gives life, not literal flesh. My teachings are spiritual food; they are life. But only to those who have faith in me — which some of you lack.' My glance took in Judas Iscariot, who would betray me. 'And such faith comes only by the drawing and enabling power of the Father.' Would they open their hearts to the Father? Be my followers, even if it meant no more handouts, no political and social liberation? Even if it meant becoming like me — humble, servant of an invisible kingdom, one rejected by those held in high esteem?

They were backing away from me, these people who had enthusiastically followed me and called themselves my disciples. 'He's no Messiah! He admits it! He refused the throne of David because he knows he's not the promised one! He's just a mystic talking in riddles!' Cultured accents, the voices of leading men . . . and now everyone was eager to show that he never took me seriously. Jeers, catcalls, laughter . . . I made no attempt to check their going. I had been rejected in Jerusalem and Judea; now I was being rejected in Galilee.

I looked at my twelve men. They had been growing progressively more appalled and confused. Yesterday more than ten thousand people were calling me their King; now all was lost, as man judges in such matters. The crisis was upon them.

'Do you also want to leave?' I asked quietly.

Peter had to clear his throat before he could find his voice.

'Lord . . . to whom could we go? The knowledge of eternal life . . . is with you. We believe . . . in fact, we know, that you are the Holy One of God.'

Later John came to me almost furtively, making sure he was not overheard.

'Lord, I don't understand. This eating your flesh and drinking your blood . . . Moses forbade the eating of flesh with blood in it.'

'Not Moses. I used Moses as my spokesman.' I sighed. John would progress spiritually further than any other man among these twelve, but even he was slow. 'Didn't I explain my symbolic language by plainly saying that the flesh counts for nothing, it is spiritual food that counts — my teachings?'

He stared. 'But Lord . . . if it's so simple, why then . . . ?'

'Why use symbols and figures at all? Because the people were not prepared to accept my simple statements. But the symbols will haunt them. Every time they eat bread they will remember the five loaves that fed ten thousand people, and my words that I am the bread from heaven.'

'I see, Lord. But you did say we must eat your flesh and drink your blood . . . '

'You must assimilate my life and character. That, John, is *true faith*.'

TO PHOENICIA 41

The tide had turned against me in Galilee; I needed a pause, a rest; my disciples needed to have their vision widened; and there was a pagan woman of remarkable character who desperately needed my help.

We set out on foot, going north-west for one and a half

days until from the hills we could look out over Phoenicia. In the distance we could just make out Sidon, and not far below us was the city of Tyre. We sat looking at the heathen temples, and thought of the spiritual darkness that lay over this extensive plain along the Mediterranean.

The Spirit had shown me the woman. She was a Canaanite. Every time she saw her daughter having an attack, foaming at the mouth and racked with spasms, she felt as if she could die. She submitted the child to the idols in the temples, receiving no help. She prayed to her gods that the sickness might be put on her instead of her child, and vainly paid for incantations.

Jewish friends told her about Jesus of Nazareth, who was healing all through Galilee without fanfare and without accepting money. Her hopes roused, she determined to search me out in Galilee and plead her child's case.

I went to the Jewish home in Tyre where there was a knowledge of my work. Amid excitement we were invited to share a meal with the people.

'Please don't spread the news that I am here,' I asked, wishing for as much seclusion as possible.

Two hours later we bade our hosts farewell. I knew that the news of our arrival had been carried to the woman with the sick child. 'No need to go and track him down in Galilee — he's right here!' Heart hammering, she was on her way. Within minutes we should meet her on the road . . . .

There she was, hurrying towards us, surprised to find that we were a group of thirteen.

'Sirs,' I heard her say to James and Andrew at our head, 'you are from Galilee . . . ?'

They did not deny it, pushing on, unwilling to speak to a heathen woman.

'Wait!' She swung round to keep up with them. 'Please! Tell me, is one of your men called Jesus of Nazareth? Or is he in another group?'

They gave her a surprised look and strode on without replying. Snubbed, she halted. John drew level with her.

'Sir!' She put out a hand to his arm, held back as she remembered just in time that a Jew did not allow himself to be touched by a non-Jew. Scurrying to keep up with him, she said, 'Please! Where can I find Jesus of Nazareth?'

He took two more strides before relenting. 'This is the master, Jesus of Nazareth,' he mumbled with a jerk of his head.

She stared at me wide-eyed, hardly daring to believe John's words. As I passed she gave me a penetrating look.

'Master!' she said hoarsely at my side. Remembering what she had heard about me, she exclaimed, 'Lord, Son of David!'

My disciples were watching, amazed at this form of address from her lips and annoyed that she was bothering me. For two reasons I walked on. I wanted to leave a picture in the minds of the disciples — a picture of their kind of heartless behaviour towards heathen people. And her faith needed to be further tested and demonstrated . . . and immortalized.

'Son of David, have mercy on me! My daughter is in agony, suffering terribly from demon possession!'

As a rabbi from the Sanhedrin would have done, I plodded on without giving her a glance.

'Get away, leave the master alone!' Peter barked at her.

Her hands hovered over my arm. 'Lord, please, you must heal my child!'

Other travellers were now gathering, staring at us. Embarrassed, Peter appealed to me, 'Lord, send her away. She's drawing attention with her cries.' Others mumbled support for him.

I stopped, said gently, 'I was only sent to the lost sheep of Israel.'

She went down on her face at my feet. The words broke

like a groan from her body, 'Lord, you must help me! Please, help me!'

'It is not right to take the children's bread and throw it to the . . . puppies.' Gentle word; subtle encouragement.

She knew that in Jewish eyes she was a dog. My words were the cue for her to shrink back, lose heart, trouble us no further . . . go back to her incurable daughter.

Instead she hung on to my feet. 'Yes, Lord! But even the dogs are fed on the crumbs that fall from their masters' table!'

It was a moment electric with faith, a moment that would live till the end of time.

'You are a woman of great faith,' I said. 'Your request is granted.'

She was motionless as the words sank in. Then her eyes were wet with tears as she struggled to her feet.

'Thank you, oh, thank you, Lord!' The words were scarcely a whisper. She gave me a lingering look of gratitude, turned and began to run. Once she flung a look over her shoulder. Her face was radiant with happiness, and then I could no longer see her clearly through my own tears.

My disciples were stunned. When will you realize, friends, that I am for all people equally? Hasn't this woman proved to you that she is no dog, but a child like yourselves?

THE DEAF-MUTE   42

To let my disciples see the spiritual needs of these heathen people, I led them north to Sidon before turning east and south. We made our long way round the eastern shore of the Lake of Galilee into the district of Decapolis.

Heathen country, this, where the two demon-possessed men had been healed. As a result of their witnessing for the past nine or ten months, virtually all normal activity now ceased as thousands began to flock to me.

A man was brought, deaf from birth, whose desperate attempts to speak resulted in strange grunts that here and there resembled words. He looked bewildered, not knowing what to make of me. I led him away from those who would too easily attach magical meanings to the procedure, unusual to me, which I was about to follow.

Putting a finger into each deaf ear, I told him with my eyes, 'I will give you hearing, friend,' and saw hope born in him. Spitting the faintest suggestion of saliva on to my finger, I touched his tongue with it to convey the message, 'Your tongue will speak like mine.' I glanced up to direct his thoughts to God and heaven, and saw his hope changing to faith.

He, a deaf pagan, spiritually blind, had faith! My thoughts veered to my own people, blessed with heaven's abundant light, yet rejecting heaven's Gift with scorn; and I sighed at the sudden stab of pain.

'Be opened!' I ordered the deaf ears.

As the sounds of life burst upon the man's mind he was overwhelmed. He stared at me in an agony of amazement and joy. Then he was looking heavenward and praising God with full-hearted fluency.

'Don't talk about your healing until I've left these regions,' I urged, trying to ward off a flood of attention focused on the physical rather than the spiritual needs of men.

But nothing could stop the words tumbling from his lips as he rushed back to the crowd.

FOUR THOUSAND FED 43

The people had brought food, prepared to stay a day or two and see if the testimony of the zealous cured demoniacs was true; and there were new arrivals all the time. I went up a hillside, sitting down to teach them, and there we slept that night.

All through the next day we remained. People were still coming, but no one left. They presented all their sick for healing and were beside themselves with amazement at the results. Twice during the day we stopped teaching and healing so that the people could dig into their baskets for something to eat.

Late on the third day I motioned my disciples closer.

'It is time for us to go. We'll take a boat and cross the lake.'

They nodded, eager to get away from the Gentile crowd, feeling contaminated after three days with them.

'But there's a problem,' I said, testing their compassion. 'Most of them had their last food yesterday. They've had nothing today, and some of them have a long way to go. I don't want to send them away hungry. Not hungry.'

Three months ago I had miraculously provided food for five thousand men and their womenfolk and children . . . but those were Jews. Not for a moment did it enter my disciples' heads that I might be considering doing the same for Gentiles.

'Four thousand men, not counting the women and children, I'd say,' Peter shrugged, eyes on the lake, already moving in that direction. 'In such an out-of-the-way place, where could we get enough bread for a crowd of that size?'

The other disciples had also dismissed the crowd in their own minds. They picked up the large baskets in which they had been carrying our food through the Gentile regions, and started after Peter.

'Wait!' I said. 'How much food do you have left?'

Puzzled, they poked about in the baskets. 'Seven loaves of bread and a couple of small fish, Master.'

The people, seeing my disciples starting off, were reluctantly getting ready to leave.

'Be seated, all of you!' I called to them, regretting that the grass, so lush three months ago, no longer carpeted the earth.

The disciples stared, hardly able to believe that I would repeat for Gentiles the mass miracle which had left them and the other Jews in such a glow of exultation that they wanted to crown me King.

Motioning for the loaves and tiny fish, I gave thanks, divided, handed to the disciples. Soon all were happily eating while exuberantly discussing the miracle of the abundant food, of which seven basketfuls remained after all had had as much as they wanted.

The bread had been Jewish bread. Would the disciples understand this: When their compatriots rejected the bread of life, it would be offered to the Gentiles?

THE MESSIAH   44

As far as possible, I was now avoiding conflict with the Jewish leaders and religious spies by keeping clear of Galilee. In addition I needed time just with my disciples, to prepare them for the coming crisis.

Moving a hard day's hike north to Caesarea Philippi, I went up into a hill alone early one morning to pray. Vividly the Spirit brought up in my mind that which I had seen in minute detail before coming to this earth as Son of Man — the insults awaiting me, the torture, crucifixion. Also the confusion and panic that would scatter my disciples. For hours I prayed for them, that they might survive the ordeal, might even now be prepared to receive my words — words designed to strengthen them later.

'What are your impressions of this country?' I asked them when I came down the hill.

They shook their heads. 'Wherever I look, superstition,' said one. 'Idols, images, ceremonies to appease gods and buy good responses from them . . . '

'Yes, spiritual darkness,' I agreed. 'And you are the bearers of light.'

'As we moved about Judea and Galilee, what were the people saying about the Son of Man?' I continued, knowing what the answer would be. 'What, or who, was the Son of Man in their judgement?'

'Some took you for John the Baptist,' Peter grinned.

'Or Elijah,' said John. 'Or Jeremiah brought to life, or some other prophet.'

I looked at Nathanael, wonderfully sincere and truehearted Nathanael who became the first disciple, more than two years ago, to confess, 'You are the Son of God! You are the King of Israel!' Now his faith shone undimmed in his steady gaze.

Less vibrantly, Andrew and Philip and Peter had also accepted this from our early days together — and now with all but one of the disciples it was an unvoiced conviction. In this circle I was *not* merely a prophet!

'But what about you men?' I asked quietly. 'Who do *you* say I am?'

To nods from the others, Peter said, 'You are the Messiah, the Son of the living God!'

'You are fortunate to know this, Simon. It was not human acumen that brought you to this conviction. My Father in heaven revealed it to you.'

Often I spoke in parables and riddles when trying to lock something into the minds of my hearers. This I did a few days ago when I said to my disciples, 'Be on your guard against the yeast of the Pharisees and Sadducees.' If instead of 'yeast' I had said 'teachings' they would have agreed and at once allowed their minds to rove to other matters. But the word 'yeast' puzzled them and provoked discussion.

When they came to a false conclusion, I repeated, 'What I say to you is: Be on your guard against the yeast of the Pharisees and Sadducees!' Not the explanation they expected; just a reiteration! By the time they saw my meaning the lesson had put down roots in their minds.

At this moment I would use the enigma form of

teaching again. It would in centuries to come launch millions of discussions — was I referring to myself, or to Peter, or to his confession of me? Sadly, many would, as did *all* my apostles with my 'yeast' statement, take their stand *contrary* to my mind. But my purpose would be served through the study, prayer, and debate devoted to the subject. All this would be one factor in sorting out those wholly surrendered to the guidance of the Spirit, wholly committed to the *total* teaching of my Scriptures, from those not so surrendered and committed.

Deliberately I said, 'Yes, it is my Father who has enabled you to say that I am the Messiah. Just so I say that you are Peter. And on this rock I will build my Church so that the powers of death will not overcome it.'

I looked at these humble, poor, unpromising-looking men and thought of the twelve foundations of the New Jerusalem on which the names of almost all twelve were to be inscribed. Was any more important work ever given to man than that which I was entrusting to them? Into their feeble hands I had been putting the keys of the *kingdom of grace*, in which men were invited to live now, in this life, in preparation for the life to come. These were 'keys of knowledge', as I would call them in five months' time — keys of salvation knowledge. Using these keys they would follow heaven's dictates in declaring what was required or prohibited. In two weeks' time they would again hear of this responsibility which I was putting upon them; now, as I still faced Peter, they heard it for the first time:

'I will give you the keys of the kingdom of heaven. Whatever you require or prohibit on earth will have been required or prohibited in heaven.'

I was giving authority and great responsibility. I had already expressed my gravest displeasure at the churchly practice of tampering with heaven's revealed will. My words, 'In vain do they worship me, teaching as doctrines the commandments of men', were plain and potent. And I had warned that many preachers of my word would in the judgement day protest at their exclusion, pointing to all the remarkable things — even miracles — which they had done in my name; and I would say to them, 'I never knew you — depart from me.' Yes, my men would have to hew to the Word; to exalt traditions of men that neutralized my commands, would ever be an abomination to me. In faith and morals they must teach men to observe all the things I had commanded . . . nothing more, nothing less. My principles were as unchangeable as I was eternal.

'Now,' I said, 'in the matter of my being the Messiah — make very, very sure that you do not talk to people about this!'

They stared, but now was not the time to explain that to our Jewish nation 'Messiah' meant a leader who would oust the foreign troops, not someone who would deliver from sin. I must to the close of my ministry avoid public discussion of my Messiahship. That was one reason why I had silenced the evil spirits when they called me 'the Holy One of God'. I must raise no political hopes; the politics of liberation I was determined to shun like sin. I had come to give man victory over himself and mortality — not over other men.

And now I must prepare my disciples for my death and apparent defeat.

'Listen carefully, friends. The Son of Man must go to Jerusalem and suffer much at the hands of the elders, chief priests and teachers of religion. Do you remember that John the Baptist called me the Lamb of God? What does that mean? John himself did not fully know. It means the Messiah must lay down his life to save those who have forfeited theirs. He will be killed. On the third day he will be raised to life.'

Peter had his hand on my shoulder. I allowed him to draw me to one side. His face was agitated.

'Never, Lord, never! This can never be allowed to happen to you!'

I turned my back on him. Facing the other disciples I said to Peter, 'Out of my sight, Satan! You are a stumbling block to me!' He was a spokesman for the powers of darkness. 'You do not think as God thinks, but as men think!'

People who knew about my arrival had been hesitantly gathering nearby. I called them closer and said to all, 'Anyone who wants to be a follower of mine will have to renounce his selfish plans for himself, take up his cross, and in character reveal me to the world. Whoever clings to self will lose his life; whoever yields his life will find it. What sense is there in a man's gaining the whole world — at the cost of his soul? Or what can he give to buy back his soul?'

For now this was enough of leaving self behind, of cross-bearing. For their encouragement I must point them to the final glory.

'The Son of Man will come in the glory of his Father with his angels. Then he will see to it that everyone gets what he deserves — according to what he had done in this life.'

The 'glory of the Father' had a strange and distant ring for them; yet Peter, James and John would soon be given a glimpse of it. 'Believe me, there are some standing here who will not die before witnessing the Son of Man coming in his kingdom.'

TRANSFIGURED 45

To keep crowds from monopolizing the instruction time which my disciples now needed so urgently, we had to keep on the move and avoid towns and villages as we went down into Galilee again. My men did not yet understand the nature of my kingdom, nor were their hearts really changed. In addition to speaking on these matters, I emphasized:

'You must take this to heart. The Son of Man is going to

be *betrayed* into the hands of men. They will kill him, and after three days he will rise.'

Although my words worried them, they did not really believe that what I was saying was inevitable. The deeper meaning of their own sacrificial system at the temple, where sin-offerings symbolically freed them from their gilt, was still foreign to them. They saw no need for heaven's Lamb to die in order that sinners could escape death. If only I would accept David's throne, all would be well! They were careful to ask no questions, fearing that this would confirm me in what they saw as my obsession with death.

Instead, they straggled along behind, talking about who should occupy the most important positions once I set up my kingdom. This was becoming a pressing matter to them. I had said I was soon to go to Jerusalem; surely that was when I'd set up my kingdom!

About a week earlier I said there were some among them who would witness the Son of Man coming in His kingdom. The time had come for this to happen.

As twilight came I selected Peter, James and John, the three who came closer than their fellow disciples to understanding the doctrines I taught. It had been a hard day of trudging from place to place, stopping only when people who wanted to hear something of my teachings, or pleaded for healing, caught up with us. Tired as we were, I led the three up the mountain until we were groping in the faint moonlight and my body, like theirs, was crying out for rest.

'I want to go aside for prayer,' I said, and they knew I wished them to watch in prayer with me.

A few paces away I went down on my knees. First I meditated on the love of my Father, then began to pray. After a while the three men could hear my voice and make out that I was praying for strength to face the test and suffering that lay ahead. As the night wore on I began to pray for my disciples. At just about that time my three friends, tired out and desperately sleepy, dozed off and failed to hear how I was pouring out my heart on their behalf.

While the hours came and went and the dew settled on us there on the hill, my disciples slept on. They were in terrible danger, and needed all the help heaven could give. At last I began to pray that they might be strengthened by seeing my divine glory.

My prayer was heard. The darkness gave way to a flood of heavenly light, turning the mountaintop brighter than noonday. Divinity within flashed forth to meet the divinity from above. I had been prostrate, and now stood up in the majesty of the kingdom of glory.

Elijah, representing the living righteous at the second coming of the Son of Man, came to my side. With him appeared Moses, representative of those saints who pass through death.

We talked about the sufferings that lay ahead for me. We discussed the vicarious death, and the glory afterwards; and when we had virtually finished, the disciples awoke.

Dazed by the light and glory and majesty, they lay transfixed and heard the names of the heavenly visitors as I spoke. After a while Peter staggered to his feet.

'Lord,' he mumbled, 'it is wonderful to be here. If you wish, I'll build three huts — one for you, one for Moses and one for Elijah.'

By allowing themselves to fall asleep the three men had lost two blessings — sharing in my self-denial, and hearing the discussion. But I was glad that they could still be eye-witnesses of my majesty and kingdom. This entering into my eternal glory was, in miniature, the second coming — that blessed hope of the ages.

A bright cloud suddenly appeared above the disciples. From it came a voice before which the mountain shook. As the disciples fell down they heard the words:

'This is my Son, whom I love. In him is my delight. Listen to him!'

They knew, now with more than faith, that I was indeed the Messiah, recognized as such by the entire heavenly universe.

I touched them. 'Get up. Do not be afraid.' Trembling, they peered over their shoulders. My heavenly guests were gone. 'Let us go!'

THE DEMONIAC BOY

At sunrise I led the way down, going slowly. When Moses received the Ten Commandments from me on Mount Sinai, so much glory shone from his face when he returned that the people were afraid to go near him; and after the heavenly glory on this mountain I was allowing time for the light to fade from our faces before we reached the crowd below.

In the grip of a deep awe, the three disciples followed at a little distance. Over my shoulder I said, 'Do not tell anyone what you have seen — not until the Son of Man has risen from the dead.' Only then would the other disciples be ready for this knowledge.

They puzzled among themselves over the meaning of 'risen from the dead', eventually shrugging the subject aside for another.

'Lord, why do the teachers of the Scriptures say that Elijah must first come?' Elijah had just appeared in confirmation of my Messiahship; but wouldn't Malachi's prophecy have been more neatly fulfilled if Elijah had come before my birth instead of only now?

'Most certainly, Elijah does come first and restores all things. But the Scriptures also say that the Son of Man must suffer much and be rejected. Do you understand *that?*

'As far as "Elijah" is concerned, he has already come. The religious leaders did not recognize him but vented their spite on him. In the same way the Son of Man is going to suffer at their hands.'

Only then did they remember that I regarded John the Baptist as the predicted 'Elijah', restorer of right doctrine and the true spirit of worship.

I knew what awaited us on the plain. The nine disciples had fallen into doubt and bickering — doubt because I talked of my betrayal and death instead of enthronement as Messianic King, and bickering because of jealousy over positions of honour. They had not spent the night in prayer — not even a small part of it. They had spent time grumbling enviously against the three selected to go with me.

At first light a crowd descended on them, and a man came with his demon-possessed son and begged that they make his child well. Mindful of the power I had given them and the miracles they had performed on their Galilean tour half a year ago, they spoke up and *in my name* commanded the demon to leave the boy. In mocking response the spirit flung the boy to the ground, where he lay shrieking and convulsing.

At once the teachers of religion were on my nine men, taunting and jeering. 'So the name of Jesus is no good, is it?' they cried. 'Look at the boy, he's sicker than ever! You're nothing but a bunch of charlatans! Your leader's so-called miracles were nothing but deception! Now that you're faced with a real case of demon possession, one we ourselves can attest as genuine, your healing attempt only makes him worse! . . . '

It was a shattering experience for the nine men. Every minute was an eternity of humiliation. The teachers of God's Word swept up the feelings of the crowd until the air was full of anger and menace. The disciples' mortification turned to fear.

All trace of the glory was not yet gone from my face when I stepped into view of the crowd. There were stares, dropped jaws, men retreating. Fear was written on the faces of the religious teachers as I walked up to them.

'What is your argument with my men?' I asked.

They moved away from me without saying a word. The ordinary people began to surge closer, eyes bright with wonder. The father pushed his way to me, intense, desperate.

'Master, I brought my son. He is possessed by a spirit that robs him of speech. It seizes him, throws him to the ground. He foams at the mouth, gnashes his teeth and carries on until he is exhausted and close to death. I asked your disciples, in your absence, to drive out the spirit, but they could not do it.'

I looked at the awe-stricken crowd, the hostile teachers of religion, the disheartened disciples. Wherever I looked there was unbelief. I was filled with sorrow.

'What an unbelieving generation! How long shall I stay with you? How long must I put up with you? Bring the boy to me.'

The boy was brought and at once the angel of Satan flung him to the ground in convulsions. His arms flailed and his legs thrashed as he filled the air with unearthly shrieks.

Satan's angel was not alone. Once more I was face to face with his master, my adversary, and the eyes of the universe were focused on a battle in the age-long war.

I allowed the seizure to go on so that the people could see how serious it was, and raised my voice above the din for the benefit of the crowd, 'How long has it been like this?'

'Since childhood!' the father shouted back, all hearing his words. 'Years and years of suffering! And of violence! Often his life was in danger, with the convulsions landing him in fire, or in water deep enough to drown him!'

Overwrought, he exclaimed, 'If at all possible, if there is anything you can do, please help us!'

'If at all possible? Everything is possible to one who has faith.'

'I do believe!' In a flash of insight he burst into tears. 'Oh, help my faith where it fails!'

The crowd was growing by the minute, and this at a

time when I needed to be alone with my disciples; so without further delay I said:

'You spirit that made this boy deaf and dumb, I command you to come out of him and never go back!'

My adversary and his angels were ready for this moment, and threw all their science and power into thwarting me and holding on to their victim. If they could succeed, as they had with my disciples, my entire mission would crumble in failure.

With a blood-curdling scream the boy went into another convulsion, then lay as inert as a corpse.

Terrified whispers were heard. 'He's dead!' 'The spirit wouldn't let go!' 'The Galilean killed him!'

But I knew that the spirits had been defeated. Taking the boy by the hand, I raised him. Strength flowed into him and he stood, calm and clear-eyed, as I presented him to his father, who flung his arms about him and started praising God in a voice that choked with sobs. I looked for the teachers of religion, but like the spirits they were in retreat.

The inner circle of my disciples had been presented with a dramatic contrast. On the mountain, glory and the image of God; down on the plain, mission service in confrontation with the image of Satan. I wanted the mountaintop and the plain to be part of their experience the rest of their lives.

Later, when I was alone with my disciples, the nine wanted to know why they had been unable to drive out the demon.

'Because of your unbelief,' I said. While they dwelt on their discouragements and grievances, how could they ever have presumed to join combat with the forces of darkness? It was only by heaven's special blessing that they had been allowed to fail and suffer humiliation; otherwise Satan could have taken over and worked miracles in response to their prayer, so confirming them in their unconverted state and turning them into pious-seeming Satanic tools. Hadn't I warned them that many who cast out demons in my name and did mighty miracles would hear me say, 'Away from me, workers of iniquity — I *never* knew you'?

'Only a life actuated by prayer is a match for this kind of challenge,' I said.

And it must be the kind of prayer that fosters faith. 'If you have faith as small as a mustard seed, you will be able to say to this "mountain" ' — the driving out of that demon from the boy, or any other impassable mountain blocking your spiritual progress — ' "Move from here to there!" and it will move. Nothing will prove impossible for you.' For when the human will becomes one with the divine will, it becomes one with omnipotence.

MIRACLE TAX 47

In Capernaum I was in Peter's home when collectors of the temple tax drew him aside with the question, 'Doesn't your master pay temple tax?'

Impulsive as always, Peter said, 'Of course he does!'

He was eager to protect me against a charge of disloyalty to the temple, but had fallen into a well-prepared trap. The people considered me a prophet, and prophets — like priests and Levites — were exempt from the tax. Now my enemies could quote Peter as authority that I paid the tax . . . and thereby acknowledged that I was not a prophet!

What should Peter have said? Only recently he had acknowledged me as the Son of God, infinitely greater than priests and prophets. Now, by his reply to the men, he was denying his confession. He had missed an opportunity of defending my status, using the prophetic Scriptures, the testimony of John the Baptist, and my own words and works.

The moment he came back into the house, trailed by his interrogators, I turned to him gentle-voiced.

'How would you answer this question, Simon? From

whom do earthly kings collect duty and taxes — from their own sons, or from others?'

'From others.'

'Then the sons are *exempt!*'

A shock went through him and the men from the temple as they realized that I knew about their discussion outside.

It was not part of my mission needlessly to antagonize established authority. 'We will not offend these men. Go down to the lake and throw out your line. A fish will take your hook. Open its mouth and you will find a four-drachma coin. Give it to these men as tax for us both.'

The taxmen stared at me as though I had gone mad, and even Peter blinked uncertainly. Then they moved off to see if this impossible thing could really happen, if the first fish to bite could actually be carrying the exact amount of the tax in its mouth.

I would pay, but only in a way that proved my divine character.

When alone with the rest of the disciples, I asked, 'What were you arguing about on the way?'

They were suddenly ill at ease, amazed as often in the past that I should know what was happening behind my back. On the way they had been discussing who among them were the greatest. Now they hung their heads and said nothing.

A little later Peter came in, awe on his face. The men from the temple had slunk off stunned when the fish yielded my tax money. Before he could exclaim about the miracle, someone told him in a whisper about my question and he stared at me in embarrassment.

John was honest enough to bring the matter out into the open. 'Master, who *is* the greatest in the kingdom of heaven?'

I gestured the disciples closer. 'If anyone wants to be first, he must make himself the very last, and servant of all.'

I relived my experience in heaven. My adversary was

still there, and he and I were close to each other. He was a great luminary, brilliant, held in high esteem, endowed with a free will. He began to toy with selfish ideas, ideas that eventually became an obsession. The madness that lies at the root of selfish ambition became clear when he, a creature, wanted equality with the Creator — not in character, which is laudable, but in power, which is a fatal delusion.

The subsequent subtle propaganda campaign in the worlds above, the self-promotion, the insinuations, the war . . . it all shivered in brilliant clarity before my mind's eye.

Thus originated the kingdom, not of love — which already existed from eternity — but of force. And its basic principle was putting self first. With this my disciples were contaminated.

A shy little boy had for some time been following my every move from the doorway.

'Come closer, little friend!' I coaxed, and had him stand in front of the disciples. To them I said, 'Unless you change fundamentally and become like little children, you will *never* enter the kingdom of heaven.'

I put my arms round the child. Here was someone who was *teachable*, without preconceived ideas and biases. Here was someone avid for *growth*. In self-forgetfulness, simplicity and confiding love, he was prepared to accept me as his teacher and the one who determined how he should live his life.

'Whoever humbles himself like this child, is the greatest in the kingdom of heaven. And whoever cherishes, for my sake, a person who has these qualities, cherishes me — and whoever cherishes me is cherishing the One who sent me.'

They were now in a mood of self-distrust, and none more so than John, who felt he should tell me something. 'Master . . . we came across a man driving out demons in your name. He wasn't one of us, so we told him to stop.'

I knew that he and James had done this.

'Do not stop such a person. No one who does a work of

divine power in my name can the next moment speak against me. He who is not against us is on our side. I assure you, if anyone gives you so much as a drink of water because you are followers of the Messiah, he will definitely not go unrewarded.

'As for the man who is a cause of stumbling — by misrepresenting my character or views — to one who had by faith become one of my "little ones", it would be better for him to be thrown into the sea with a heavy millstone tied round his neck.

'What unhappiness there is in the world because such causes of stumbling arise! Come they will, but woe betide the one through whom they come!'

But sometimes the cause of stumbling is in yourself. 'If your hand or your foot causes you to sin, cut it off and fling it away.' After all, how much is eternal life worth? 'It is better for you to enter into life maimed or crippled, than to keep both hands or feet and land in the fire which you cannot quench. If your eye betrays you, tear it out and throw it away. It is better to enter into life with one eye than to keep both and land in the fire of hell.

'Everyone will be salted with fire.' Either the fiery trials of life will purify him now, or the fire of judgement will prove to be his destiny. You can be preserved only by having 'salt' in your life — the righteousness that comes from God. 'Have salt in yourselves, and be at peace with one another.

'Never despise one of my "little people". I tell you, their heavenly guardian angels always have access to my Father in heaven.

'Suppose a man has a hundred sheep and one of them strays, what do you think he does? Doesn't he leave the ninety-nine on the hillside and go in search of the one that strayed? And if he finds it, I assure you he is more delighted over that sheep than over the ninety-nine that never wandered off. Just so does your heavenly Father cherish these "little ones", wishing that not a single one of them should be lost.

'And what if one of my "little ones", sincerely struggling to live the life of faith yet weak and erring, should wrong you? Do not embarrass or shame him by talking to others; in a spirit of gentleness and meekness, go and talk to him privately.

'If your brother sins against you, go and discuss the matter with him strictly between yourselves. If he accepts your overtures, you have restored the spirit of full brotherliness. If he rejects your approach, take one or two others with you. This will allow all facts to be established on the testimony of two or three witnesses. If he refuses to listen to them, report the matter to the congregation. And if he refuses to yield to the congregation, treat him as you would an outsider.' Not with disdain or neglect — did the Son of Man not come to seek and save the lost? — but as someone who needs to be brought into fellowship with me.

Although you as a church can in no way alter God's will or law or purposes, for God does not change, yet you are acting as ambassadors of heaven, and the results of your work reach to eternity. So, 'whatever you require or prohibit on earth will have been required or prohibited in heaven. I assure you, if two of you on earth agree about any request you have to make, the request will be granted by *my Father* in heaven. For where two or three come together in my name, there am I with them.'

They would not be ambassadors cut off from the Source of their power, guidance and support. If they obeyed my Word with a sincere heart, I would be their wisdom and help.

Peter came up and asked, 'Lord, how many times am I to forgive my brother if he keeps wronging me? Up to seven times?'

'Emphatically not seven times — seventy times seven!

'You see, the kingdom of heaven is like a king who

decided to settle accounts with the men who served him. First to be brought before him was a man who owed millions. He was unable to pay so his master ordered that he, his wife, children and possessions be sold to meet the debt.

'The man knelt before him, pleading, "Be patient with me and I'll repay the debt in full!" His master, deeply moved, let him go and set aside the debt.

'But when the servant went out he came across a fellow servant who owed him a small sum. He grabbed him by the throat, shouting, "Pay back what you owe me!"

'His fellow servant went to his knees. "Be patient with me and I will repay you!" he pleaded.

'He refused and had the man thrown into prison until the debt was settled. The other servants, deeply shocked, reported everything to their master.

'The master called the servant and said, "You scoundrel, I waived your debt when you pleaded with me. Weren't you bound to do the same by your colleague?" And in anger the master handed him over to the law until he should pay back all he owed.

'This is how my heavenly Father will deal with you unless you each forgive your brother from your heart.'

SECRET JOURNEY 48

Summer had ended and my brothers with whom I had grown up in Nazareth were getting ready to go to Jerusalem for the Feast of Tabernacles. Hearing that I was showing no signs of doing the same, they sought me out.

'Why hide away in these backwoods towns?' they wanted to know. 'Doing your mighty deeds for mere peasants and fisherman will get you nowhere. If you've really been doing all the things we've heard about, Jerusalem is the place for you! There you'll catch the eye of the people who really count — priests, rabbis, teachers of the law, members of the Sanhedrin.'

Although the quality of my life had over the years been a mystery to them, they did not believe in my Messiahship. They believed in the great, famous, learned men of the nation — and these men rejected me. I had made a disastrous mistake, they felt, in estranging men so powerful, instead of wooing their support.

And why were they so eager that I by some strange miracle succeed? Because then they could bask in my glory; then they would overnight turn into the influential brothers of a nationally acclaimed leader.

I replied, 'The right time for me has not yet come. For you, of course, one day is as good as another, to leave for the Feast.

'You go to the Feast. I am not yet ready to go, because the right moment has not arrived.'

After they had gone I also left, choosing a little used route. I wanted no cheering crowd awaiting me at Jerusalem's gates. This could force the authorities' heavy hand and precipitate the crisis which was still half a year away.

I knew the state of things in Jerusalem. The Jewish leaders were hunting high and low for me, hoping for a chance to condemn me. For fear of them no one was willing to speak of me as the Messiah. Some defended me as a prophet, others called me a charlatan. Those who were for me tended to speak in whispers.

The first day of the week-long Feast started, and it became clear that I was not there.

'Ah, he's afraid of the priests and rabbis and rulers!' It was a cry that quickly spread throughout the city — a cry of derision. Some of the more thoughtful people called me sensible: it was as much as my life was worth to show my face here in the stronghold of my deadly enemies.

And then, halfway through the Feast, I walked alone into the city.

Everywhere the people had built shelters, 'tabernacles' or booths, of leafy branches — in the valleys, on the hills, in the streets, even on the flat housetops. No one lived in a house. The entire city, even the eminent religious and secular leaders, as well as Jews from distant lands who had come for the Feast, were reliving the forty years' tent life of the Exodus. Jerusalem was a forest of greenery, and alive with people.

Some gave the thirty-three-year-old man in peasant garb a second glance, puzzled, wondering where they had seen him before. On the whole I was ignored. I looked into their faces and heard snatches of conversation.

The nearly four days had been full of priestly pomp and ceremony, full of music and processions. Yet the people were starving.

Here was a burdened, aching mind; there sorrow, or secret despondency, or a deep grief. Everywhere, a restless longing, an underlying and often unconscious soul hunger. At first there had been a magic for them in the ceremonies; now everything felt mechanical, and the gnawing was back, more insistent than ever. Their lives were hollow, their religion did not change their 'hearts' — motive, purpose in life, character.

'The Messiah . . . Messiah . . . Messiah.' This was a name I heard everywhere. A whole generation had been in a state of expectancy. I heard men arguing about the Messiah, the prophecies, the man from Nazareth who proclaimed the kingdom of heaven and worked miracles, even bringing the dead to life, yet had not been seen in Jerusalem in eighteen months, who had been expected here but had kept away because the leaders wanted to kill him. . . .

It was almost impossible to get into the temple court, there was such a crush of people. They were singing, waving branches of palm and myrtle, and shouting hosannas under direction of a choir of Levites ranged on both sides of the white steps of the temple.

I mounted the fourteen steps of the inner sacred area, turned and faced the crowd . . . the only one not singing, swaying, waving branches, shouting. Voices in full swell began to waver and stumble. The swaying and waving stopped, and from mouths still open came no sound. The choir alone hung on to its notes, and then it faltered and dragged to a ragged end.

I raised a hand to salute these staring faces, these poor hungry hearts, and started speaking. Reaching into the past, I led my audience to the side of Abraham as he listened to God's voice. Together we left Egypt under the ten plagues. With Moses we mounted Sinai to receive from the divine Deliverer the tables of the Ten Commandments that were for mankind, and the laws of sacrifices that pointed to the Messiah who should 'see of the travail of his soul' and by his supreme sacrifice 'justify many, for he shall bear their iniquities', as Isaiah said.

I reached into the future and showed them things earthly and heavenly, and the Son of Man who was also Son of God coming in divine glory with myriads of angels as King of kings and Lord of lords.

Returning to the present, I warned my audience in ringing tones that the kingdom of heaven announced by John the Baptist was with them, and rejection of it would lead to the destruction of their proud city and its temple. I pleaded with them to walk in the light which Heaven had been shedding on them since the Baptist started preaching, and to have a hand in nothing they would later regret.

While I spoke, priests, rabbis and other teachers of religion had appeared and now formed a phalanx of impressive men just below me, frowning as they heard the people exclaiming, 'How did this man get such learning without ever having studied in the rabbinical schools?' Hard-faced and cold-eyed, they held a quick whispered consultation among themselves, then in a body marched halfway up my steps.

'You, sir!' their loud-voiced spokesman challenged. 'Who gave you authority to preach?'

Clever. My message could now be swept aside in a heated debate on a technical point, a matter of convention.

'My teaching is not my own. It comes from him who sent me. Those who really want to do God's will, will discern whether my teaching comes from God or from myself.'

My reply, going much beyond their question, caught them off-stride. Did I mean truth could never be found except by the one who means to follow it once God reveals it to him? Or did I mean they failed to recognize God's truth in me because they themselves were out of harmony with God?

I meant both.

I would give them — and the crowd — a test by which to distinguish a heaven-sent teacher from a self-appointed one.

'The self-appointed preacher fixes attention on himself.' Sooner or later he betrays his self-seeking spirit. 'But if everything a man does only fixes attention on the One who sent him, he is sincere and reliable.'

They had abruptly run out of questions. Recently I was shown these men plotting against me with pious remarks about the need to protect God's people against deception, the need — in defence of the most holy faith — to catch me on a charge that would lead to my death. In an effort to save them from themselves, I would give them a sign of divinity. I would reveal that I knew their secret.

'Through Moses you received the law, did you not? Yet . . . not a single one of you is keeping it!' Priests, teachers of the law — they stared at my blankly. Lowering my voice I said, 'You are all involved in murder — a plot to get me killed!'

I saw the blanching, the involuntary recoiling. I was coupling God's command 'You shall not kill' with their scheming for my elimination . . . a scheming open to my eye! I saw momentary terror in more than one face; then a hardening, a pride-threatened, blind recklessness.

'You must be devil-possessed!' they shouted, and some in the crowd parroted the cry. 'Who is trying to kill you?'

They knew. They also knew that they now stood exposed in their own eyes and one another's as liars . . . these poor, desperate men. They were men of religion, yes — but also men of deep-seated prejudices. Their hatred of me had been implacable since I cured the paralysed man at the Pool of Bethesda eighteen months ago — on the Sabbath day, moreover, which concerned another of those commands I gave them through Moses on Sinai.

'I know what is rankling with you. You cannot get over the miracle I did here, on the Sabbath. How can it have been wrong for me to heal a man's entire suffering body, when you yourselves go out of your way on the Sabbath to attend to just one part of the body — in circumcision? Stop judging superficially! Be fair!'

I came down the steps and my enemies opened for me. As I moved through the crowd I heard men exclaiming, 'But this is the man they've been getting ready to kill! Yet here he's speaking openly and no one dare arrest him!'

'Can it be that our rulers know he's the Messiah?' voices asked.

'No! We know the origins of this man. When the Messiah comes, no one will know anything about his origins!'

Still in the temple's outer court, I raised my voice.

'Yes, you know me, and know where I come from! But I did not come merely of my own accord. I was sent by One who is the embodiment of truth, One whom you don't know! I know him, because I originate from him!'

'Blasphemy!' the priests exploded, desperately trying to incite the crowd to lay hold of me; but not a hand was raised.

I made my slow way out of the city, knowing that many had decided for me and were saying, 'When the Messiah comes, can anyone expect him to be more convincing than this man?'

TEACHING IN THE TEMPLE

The next day I was back, teaching at the temple, conscious of the spies who followed me about, but even more conscious of the spiritual needs of the people.

The Pharisees had called for a meeting of the Sanhedrin. There it was decided to send some of the temple police to arrest me — but in private, so as to avoid a clash with the crowd. How I longed to reach the hearts of these officers!

After speaking for an hour on heaven's kingdom of grace, I said, 'I shall be here with you for only a short while. Then I return to the One who sent me. You will search for me, but I shall be *beyond your reach*. Where I am you will be unable to go.'

At the words 'beyond your reach', I looked at the men biding their time to arrest me. They were in acute discomfort.

Close to them a group of rabbis sneered, 'Where does he intend going, to be beyond our reach? Is he going to join our people scattered among the heathen nations — will he teach the Greeks, the *heathen?*'

I knew they had been hard at work spreading their concept of the Messiah. Isaiah's 'The Lord of hosts will reign on Mount Zion and in Jerusalem, and will manifest his glory among his courtiers' was one of the scriptures they used to show that the impoverished Galilean was a nobody and a false prophet. They were impressive, zealous . . . and mistaken, failing to see the dual nature of the Messiah's coming. The Spirit of God had not been able to get past their prejudices to teach them a correct under-standing of Scripture.

'What's behind his words, "You will search for me, but I shall be beyond your reach"?' they were still growling among themselves.

I would be with them a short while — half a year. Then, my ascension to my Father where they could not go. And in the judgement day they would 'search' for me, yearn to have me to save them, and find me unreachable. Then they would cry in Jeremiah's words, 'The harvest is past, the summer is ended, and we are not saved!'

On the last morning of the Feast I watched the priest performing the ceremony that was a reminder of the rock, struck by Moses in the wilderness, that yielded a stream of water. I was the Rock, struck by the people and for the people; and my words were the water of life . . . but neither priest nor people knew this. As the water was poured into a silver bowl at the altar, and the wine — my blood, my death — into the second bowl, I went forward and faced the people.

'Is there a thirst in you?' I cried. 'If so, come to me and drink! Whoever believes in me, as Scripture says, shall have streams of living water flowing from his inner being!'

I left them to ponder these words — some to reject them with scorn, but others joyfully coming to see in them heaven's offer of salvation.

As I moved away some were calling me 'the prophet' and 'the Messiah'. Others demurred: 'How can the Messiah come from Galilee? The Scriptures point to King David's lineage, and Bethlehem!'

Some were inclined to help the temple police arrest me, yet not a hand was raised. The police themselves were unnerved, and later had to face the sharp question from the chief priests and Pharisees in the Sanhedrin, 'Why didn't you bring him in?'

'Because . . . because . . . ' Really, because pride and

prejudice had not blinded them. They could find no words to describe their feelings, and blurted out, 'Nobody ever spoke the way this man does!'

'What! Have you also been taken in by him? How *could* you? Has any important person, any leading figure, accepted him? Not a single one! The only ones who have accepted him are the ignorant — and by doing so they're bringing nothing but trouble on themselves!'

They began to lay new plans to rid the nation of me, but this time Nicodemus was present. He overcame his caution sufficiently to ask, 'Does our law condemn a man without first giving him a hearing?'

Startled, they flung at him, 'Are you also from Galilee? Look into it and you'll see Galilee is the last place to look for a prophet!'

They adjourned; and Nicodemus the rabbi was now a marked man.

THE ADULTERESS 50

Later that day a religious leader saw a way to bring me into conflict either with the Roman authorities or the authority of Moses. A plot was hatched and a very charming young man of loose morals summoned, assured of immunity from prosecution, and sent off on his vile errand.

From this was to come an episode perfectly typical of my work and the spirit in which it was done — in a way, an epitome of my actions.

I spent the night on the Hill of Olives, and the next morning returned to the temple, sat down, and taught the people.

After a while a group of religious leaders fought their way through the crowd, dragging a woman whose eyes were wide with terror. They picked her up and shoved her forward so that she stood trembling between them and me.

'Teacher,' said their florid-faced leader, a man of great influence, 'we have caught this woman in the very act of adultery! Now, in the law Moses commanded us to stone such women. What do you say should be done?'

If I said, 'Carry out the law of Moses', I could be charged with usurping the authority of Rome and within an hour be in prison like John the Baptist. But they knew how willing I was to forgive, and expected me to speak for leniency. Then they could turn to the crowd and thunder, 'This fellow sets aside the explicit command of Moses! Shouldn't he be stoned for contempt of our inspired traditions?'

I looked at the leader. He was guilty before God of having plotted this act of immorality. Those men with him were his co-conspirators. With them, uncharged with any offence, was the man whom they had got to seduce this woman.

I bent down and in the thick dust on the paving traced the words: Sexual entrapment.

'Well, what do you say?'

They thought I was pretending deafness. I looked up. That man next to the leader was guilty of corruption. In the dust I wrote: Accepting bribes.

My gaze found the third man and I wrote: A vile temper.

For the fourth man I was writing 'Secret acts of lust' when their leader impatiently pushed past the woman to read what I had written. 'Sexual entrapment.' I looked him in the eye and he knew with chilling certainty that I was aware of his discussions with his cronies, of the summoning of the roué, the promise of immunity . . . that I could expose him before this crowd.

'This is my verdict,' I said. 'Let the one among you who is without guilt throw the first stone.'

Florid face swallowed, edged his way into the crowd and disappeared fuming and humiliated.

I was still writing their record of sin in the dust when the last accuser, having peered over my shoulder, nervously made off.

I straightened up.

'Woman, where are those men? Has no one remained to condemn you?'

'No one, sir,' she said with a catch in her voice.

'Nor do I condemn you. Go, and turn your back on your life of sin.'

She fell down at my feet, sobbing her heart out . . . .

TRUE LIGHT 51

One of the striking things about the Feast of Tabernacles was the ceremony of lights. After the evening sacrifice all the great high-placed lamps were lit in one of the temple courts, and while ruler and ruled joined in festive dancing the sacred light shone over all Jerusalem. It reminded believers of the pillar of light that guided Israel in the time of Moses, and was accepted by the people as a promise of the coming Messiah.

'The ceremony of lights is impressive, but inadequate,' I said to John early in the morning at the temple; and when a crowd had gathered I pointed to the rising sun as a more fitting symbol and said:

'*I* am the light of the world!' I was now plainly stating my Messiahship. 'Whoever follows me will never grope in the dark. He will have the light of life!'

Whatever true light — of religion, philosophy or science — has ever shone on this planet, came from God. Whether it shone faintly or brightly, it had only one Source. And I was now claiming to be the one, designated by heaven, through whom the light of truth and life reached mankind.

The crowd buzzed with discussion of my claim. Many were beginning to believe, and to them I said, 'If you hold on to what I have told you, you will be true disciples of mine. You will know the truth, and the truth will set you free!'

The religious leaders present exclaimed indignantly, 'What do you mean, set us free? We *are* free, totally free!'

How irrational — they were even at this moment unfree, subjects of Rome. But more, they were planning to kill their Messiah: they were slaves of Satan.

Dispassionately, with an aching heart, I murmured to these influential men, 'You are inspired by the devil: you are bent on killing me. And no one is free who has given himself to sin!'

I gazed out over a crowd hushed by the solemnity of my accusation, and referring to the second death said, 'I assure you, those who obey my teaching will never die!'

'Now we know you're mad!' the religious leaders shouted. 'Our father Abraham died, the prophets died. You, a life-giver? Are you greater than Abraham?'

'Before Abraham was, I am!' I said.

In a torrent of rage, screaming, 'Blasphemy! He makes himself God!' they scattered to the pile of rocks which Herod's men were still building into the temple complex, to stone me to death. I quietly walked into the group of believers and from there out into the city and down the Kidron valley.

BORN BLIND 52

It was Sabbath morning when, near the temple, we came across a stooped, thin, middle-aged man who was pathetically groping his way along. He had been blind from birth. My disciples, still not free from the common misunderstandings regarding God's character and actions, asked, 'Rabbi, whose sin brought blindness to this man —

his, or his parents'?' Had God pounced on him with retribution?

This was no time to remind them of the book of Job and its inspired lesson: my adversary is primarily responsible for all suffering on this planet, and God is not.

'That is not the question,' I replied. 'The question is: what will happen now? God's power will be displayed in his healing, because I am the light of the world.'

Using a little saliva and dust, I mixed clay and spread it on the eyelids of the poor sufferer — that would help his faint faith — and said, 'Go and wash in the Pool of Siloam.'

A passer-by, on tiptoe with interest, volunteered to lead him to the pool. Wanting to believe yet almost afraid, he allowed the man to take him by the hand. At the pool he washed his eyes . . . and could see.

This caused a great stir. Men hurried to see this wonder, and excitement bubbled through the city. The man was summoned to appear before the eminent men of religion.

'The fellow who did this to you is not of God!' they declared. 'The reason is clear: he does not keep the Sabbath.'

That is, as I would have pointed out, did not keep the Sabbath according to their regulations, which I had deliberately flouted by mixing the clay, by anointing the eyes, and by curing the blindness; because in my life of total obedience there was not room for the niggling traditions of men.

'But if he is a sinner, why did God work a miracle through him?' others retorted.

'This man couldn't have been blind from birth!' the leaders said, and summoned the parents.

'Are you his parents? Was he born blind? If so, how is it he can now see?'

'Yes, he is our son. Yes, he has been blind from birth.' Afraid to commit themselves beyond these undeniable facts, they said, 'How it happened that he can now see, we don't know. Ask him, he can answer for himself.'

The leaders did their utmost to intimidate and confuse the man, but he kept saying, 'If that man had not come from God he could have done nothing!' They excommunicated him from the synagogue.

I found him in the street and asked, 'Do you believe in the Son of Man?'

'Who is he, sir? If you will tell me, I am prepared to believe!' How eager he was!

'He is the one you are speaking to,' I said; and he went down in worship before me, exclaiming, 'Lord, I believe!'

'Strange,' I murmured. 'My coming makes the blind able to see, and turns the sighted blinder than they ever were . . . '

Some of those who had banished this man from his place of worship were beginning to gather — soul-shepherds of Jerusalem. Fixing my eyes on them, I spoke along these lines: 'There are some who try to get in among the sheep without having entered by the gate. There is only one proper way into the sheep pen — the gate. I am that gate! Men purporting to be shepherds have, while ignoring the gate, devised many ways of trying to get into God's sheep pen. All such attempts must fail. Whoever enters through me will be saved!

'In addition to being the gate, I am the good shepherd spoken of by Isaiah, David and Ezekiel. The good shepherd lays down his life for the sheep.

'I have other sheep not in this pen. They will hear my call and there shall be one flock and one shepherd.'

I said more in this vein, and my audience was divided, some furiously against me and others thoughtfully for me.

'The good shepherd has come that his sheep may have life, and have it to the full!' I pledged, pointing to the man born blind.

His eyes were full of light and life, full of seeing, brimming with adoration . . . and perfect happiness. He now had life to the full, because he had allowed me into the very core of his existence.

And on the question of 'Why suffering?' — what a witness he was to the true character of my Father in heaven, who said through the prophet Jeremiah, 'Yes, I have loved you with an everlasting love! That is why I have dealt with you in the kindness of *love*.'

THE GOOD SAMARITAN 53

In the presence of a Jewish audience, a theologian was persuaded to try to trap me into a statement making light of the law given on Sinai, so that the masses could be roused against me.

He caught my attention and asked, 'Teacher, what must I do to inherit eternal life?'

There was an element of sincerity in the man. I gave him a chance to provide the answer to his own question. 'What is written in the Law? How do you interpret it?'

Amazingly, he cut through all the external things — forms, creeds, ceremonies — to the core of true religion. A little tentatively he replied, 'Love the Lord your God with all your heart, with all your soul, with all your strength, and with all your mind. And love your neighbour as yourself.'

'An excellent answer,' I said. The problem was, he was not living this philosophy — most noticeably towards his fellow man. I said pointedly, 'You must do this, and you will live.'

Made uncomfortable by my manner, he asked defensively, 'And how do you define "neighbour"?'

Ah, the much-debated question! The heathen were beyond the pale, and so were Samaritans. Who then was one's neighbour, in our own Jewish society?

I reminded him of an item of news that had led to astonished comments in Jewish homes. 'A man on the way from Jerusalem to Jericho was set upon by robbers. They stripped him of his clothes and beat him senseless.

'A priest happened along, saw the man and passed by on the other side. A little later a Levite appeared, saw the man and gave him a wide berth.

'Then a Samaritan was passing when he saw the man and stopped. He treated the victim as best he could, took him to an inn and paid for his care in advance, promising to meet any extra expenses there might be.'

Now the key question. 'Which of these three, the priest, the Levite or the Samaritan, was in the true sense neighbour to the victim?'

The theologian balked at saying the word 'Samaritan', but he was honest enough to give the correct answer: 'The one who had mercy on him.'

'Go and do likewise.'

So your 'neighbour' is anyone who needs your help. And paying lip service to the principle of love was not enough. Love to God leads to obedience to him. Love to the human being who needs a service you can render will then naturally follow, as fruit of your first love . . . really, as God's love flowing through you.

As the theologian left, a disappointment to his cronies who thought he would trap me, I stared at him yearningly. Surely there was a chance that he might come to see me as the heavenly Good Samaritan who had come to rescue those bruised and battered by life and by sin, and at the cost of his own life saved those willing to be saved . . . .

TRUE VALUES
54

About four weeks after sending out the seventy, I arrived in Bethany near Jerusalem and was hospitably received in the home of Lazarus and his sisters Martha and Mary. This was my first visit here; it was not to be my last. The home was peaceful, orderly, quiet: a tiny heaven on earth. After the turmoil of jealousy and animosity outside, it was a haven for my tired spirit.

Martha was an energetic person, officious, constantly in motion. Soon after our arrival she came in from the kitchen, where she had been audibly fussing over her duties, and looked accusingly at Mary who had seated herself at my feet and was lost in my conversation about the spiritual kingdom.

'Master, look at Mary!' Martha said a little sharply. 'Don't you mind that she's left all the work to me? Won't you tell her to help me?'

I looked at the dear girl, so eternally busy that her prayer life suffered and there was hardly any time for meditating on God's Word.

'Martha, Martha,' I said gently. 'You fret and over-burden yourself in many ways. But there is one thing that is vital. Mary has given priority to this better thing, and she will always be the richer for it.'

The main purpose of this temporary life is to gain eternal life; and the way to eternal life is a true knowledge of the Life-giver.

Mary was in thrall to every word I spoke. She would gladly have given up eating for a week to get this knowledge of God. She was seeking first the kingdom of heaven. After that the things of this fleeting life would be seen to . . . and in these heaven was also interested.

It was hard to persuade Martha that her guests were not only quite undemanding, but would feel their stay in her home had been happiest if she did less for them. She sat down with Mary, as reluctant as a mother asked to sacrifice her baby; but after a while a calm devotional spirit came over her and she was leaning forward, intent on every word . . . and I was happy.

Right on time the seventy missionaries arrived to report on their work. They were overjoyed.

'When ordered in your name, Lord, even the demons obey us!'

Scenes from the past flashed before me — the war in heaven, the adversary and his army of fallen angels vanquished. I stood in silence so long that my disciples stared in wonder.

Sighing, I said, 'I saw Satan fall like a flash of lightning from heaven.' And soon, when I died faithful on the cross, he would fall even further in defeat. Yes, the great 'serpent' and his angel 'serpents' and 'scorpions' were a defeated foe, destined for annihilation; and so I added, 'I have given you power to triumph over serpents and scorpions, even to overcome all the power of the enemy without your suffering harm.

'However' — lest they lose sight of their utter constant dependence upon God, and begin to rely on their own strength and wisdom — 'do not be jubilant when you find you have power over the spirits. Rather rejoice over this: that your names are written in heaven.' To have their names, like Mary of Bethany, in the book of life — what greater blessing can there be?

I looked at these humble men all about me, men not esteemed for learning, who yet had faith and insights lacking in the religious leaders and the great men of the nations. From a full heart I exclaimed, 'Thank you, Father, Lord of heaven and earth, for revealing to these little children things incomprehensible to those regarded as wise and learned! In this your graciousness is revealed, Father.'

I turned to the disciples and the others listening. 'Everything has been put into my hands by the Father. No one knows the Son as does the Father, and no one the Father as does the Son and those to whom the Son reveals him.'

Afterwards I said to the disciples only, 'Blessed are those who understand what you understand! What prophets and kings could only predict, and that with partial understanding, you are seeing right before you.'

It was winter. Four months hence would see me in Jerusalem at the fateful Passover. Meanwhile, Jerusalem was a place to avoid. But the Feast of Dedication had just started, the city was aswarm with people, and at Bethany I was just an hour away on foot.

I slipped into the city with my disciples, and we were walking along the colonnade of Solomon at the temple when I was recognized and soon a frenetic crowd was surging around us. For half an hour or more I preached to them, and then the crowd opened for a large group of religious leaders. Their spokesman challenged me brusquely.

'How long will you mince words with us? Are you or are you not the Messiah?'

'I have given you the answer to that — one you would not accept.' I was not their kind of Messiah — leader of an uprising against Rome, liberator of the nation. I was much more.

'The miracles I perform in my Father's name speak louder than words. Why is it that you don't believe? Because you are not my sheep. My sheep listen to my voice. I know them and they follow me. I give them eternal life. When they have that, they never perish. No one can snatch them out of my hand. My Father who gives them to me is greater than any other being, and no one can snatch them out of his hand.'

I looked my questioner in the eye. He wanted a straight claim from me; he would have it.

'My — Father — and — I — are — one!'

The religious men began to tear at their hair.

'Stone this man to death!' they cried, and the crowd scattered before them as they rushed to a pile of building rocks. I stood waiting. They came staggering under the weight of rocks too big for easy handling.

'Just a moment!' I held up my hand. 'I have done

miracles in your presence, miracles performed in the name of my heavenly Father. For which of these miracles do you want to stone me?'

They halted, sensing that they did not have the crowd with them.

'Not for any of these,' they said. A remarkable statement, which admitted that I had never broken God's law by healing on the Sabbath — the very thing which had turned them apoplectic on other occasions. 'We're stoning you for blasphemy! You, a mere man, are claiming to be God!'

So they had understood me perfectly.

'If your own law applies the word "god" to judges and other mere men, how much more is "God" appropriate to the one whom the Father consecrated and sent into the world? How can you accuse me of blasphemy when I say I am the Son of God?'

They hesitated, furious but uncertain what to do. I appealed:

'Look at my miracles, my life. Unless they speak of unity with the Father, do not believe in me. But if they do, accept the evidence before you! Then you will know that the Father is in me and I am in the Father!'

This was too much for them. Screaming, they surged forward to drag me to a clearing where they could stone me. I moved into the crowd and made my escape from the city controlled by my enemies.

Perea east of the Jordan was now a refuge for me. Near where John the Baptist had preached and baptized, I taught the disciples and the crowds that came from everywhere, including Jerusalem and the rest of Judea.

These four months must not pass without my teaching the disciples all the essentials, everything of key importance concerning worship and the kingdom of heaven. My subjects included prayer, righteousness, God's infinite love, man's indifference to his own salvation, the cost of true discipleship, the dangers of materialism. I foretold my death, and for the first time publicly spoke about my second coming.

Central to it all was the Creator and wonderful Father, who loved human beings so much, even after they became rebels against his law, that he was determined to give them a chance to escape their self-inflicted doom. They were all lost: by sin, all forfeited life. The Lamb of God took their death penalty on himself, giving himself for them; and all who in return gave themselves to him were restored to life.

This self-giving required trust in God. It meant surrender of self and sin. At its core was this: a personal relationship with the Son of God who was also Son of Man. This closeness — to the point of oneness — would be the believer's only righteousness, and his victorious strength.

In my daily life they saw the way to live. They saw that the holy Scriptures meant more to me than food, that I had saturated my mind with them so that they were my vocabulary and conversation; that I sought to have my whole life dominated by the Word of God.

They saw my prayer life. They had never seen a rabbi or a priest who prayed so often or for so many hours of his daily life. But what fascinated them even more was the quality of my praying.

I loved to go aside and pray alone; but my friends knew that in public prayer and private prayer I avoided set phrases, or a learned, profound, or poetic style. To me prayer was not ceremony or incantation or a bombarding of heaven; it was intimate communion with the heavenly Father, a heart opened in sincerity, an unmechanical, vital experience, an expression of praise and reverence.

Those close to me knew that I believed in continuous prayer, so that when not engaged in public or private prayer my heart was always uplifted to my Father — no activity could break the contact.

They saw that the Father's will was the only law of my

life. I started every day in surrender, in a seeking of God's plans for me for that day; and they knew that self-seeking and ambition were never allowed to influence me by so much as a hair's breadth. I was not of this world, and they must not be of this world.

THE LOST SON 56

The Pharisees were anxious about my preaching in Perea, and its effect on the crowds that streamed from Judea and Galilee. They sent an imposing delegation that assumed a protective attitude towards me.

'For your own sake,' they said solicitously, 'leave this place and go elsewhere! We have information that Herod wants to kill you.'

They had no such information. Herod Antipas, ruler of Galilee and Perea, had killed John the Baptist about a year ago, and my miracles filled him with awe and a superstitious fear that I was the Baptist raised to life. He was eager to see me, and at the same time nervous about such a meeting.

But I would not be discourteous and show up the Pharisees' lie. They were trying to flush me out of Herod's Perea, to a Judea ruled by Pontius Pilate, where they could more easily lay hands on me.

'Go and tell that fox Herod,' I said, 'that I will be here a while longer, casting out demons and healing people until my work is completed.'

I wanted them to know that I knew they were planning my death in Jerusalem, and said with irony, 'It is unthinkable for a prophet to meet his death anywhere but *in Jerusalem!*'

On another day, glancing at the religious leaders of my nation, these men who were so sure they were right and righteous, I told a parable.

'Two men went up to the temple to pray, one a Pharisee

and the other a tax collector. The Pharisee stood up and muttered to himself, "God, I thank you that I am not like the other people — grasping, cheating, adulterous . . . like the tax collector over there. I fast on the second and fifth day each week and pay tithes on all I get!" '

And, of course, enjoyed an almost awed respect from everybody — especially on each fasting Monday and Thursday. What an upright and righteous man!

But the one who reads man's deepest thoughts viewed him in a different light. Here was someone who believed in deeds of merit as the way to life! The good that he did would weigh up against the bad, offsetting and cancelling it. A favourable balance of good deeds would commend him to a pleased God and make him a righteous man — a fundamentally pagan philosophy!

If only he had compared his life with the Life which God had sent to this world, he would have seen his highest virtues and best works as filthy rags . . . .

I went on: 'But the tax collector stood humbly at a distance. He would not even raise his eyes to heaven but beat his breast and said, "O God, have mercy on me, a man sunken in sin." '

I gazed at the 'sinners' and common people who felt so condemned when they saw the Pharisees' religiosity, then at the religious leaders.

'I tell you that this man who saw no good in himself, and could only yearn for God's goodness to enter his life, was the one who went home justified before God. Everyone who exalts himself will be humbled. Everyone who humbles himself will be exalted.'

Most of the priests, rabbis and doctors of the Law were offended, but some were clearly in two minds about me. Knowing that within four years a large number of priests would become obedient to the faith which they now opposed, I decided on a parable in three forms.

'A man has a hundred sheep. One of them goes astray,

discovers that it is lost, but does not know how to get back. The owner does not abandon his lost sheep. Leaving the ninety-nine where they are reasonably safe, he hunts high and low until he finds his sheep and carries it home. He gets all his friends to rejoice with him over the lost sheep which he recovered.

'This tells you something about your heavenly Father. He takes the initiative in saving lost man. He loves man even before man repents. He loves the one rebellious planet and goes after it.

'As the owner of the sheep gets all his friends to be glad with him, so there is more rejoicing in heaven over one sinner who repents than over ninety-nine seemingly safe and righteous souls.'

Strange how those 'seemingly safe and righteous' souls were uncomfortable in my presence and tended to bunch together off to one side. By contrast, the 'common' people who made no claim to righteousness were happily drawn to me!

'A woman has ten silver coins and loses one. She lights a lamp, sweeps her home, scrutinizes every corner until she finds it, and gets her friends to rejoice with her. I tell you, so great is the value of a soul that there is rejoicing all through the ranks of God's angels over one sinner who repents.'

And the coin, unlike the sheep, did not even know it was lost. There are humans like that. Some are outside the company of believers, others inside — and the 'inside' ones are even more lost. But, being Love, God searches even for those oblivious of their true condition.

'And then,' I went on, 'there was a man who had two sons. The younger one, weary of restraint and set on having his own way, said, "Father, give me my share of the estate!" The father, a wise, gentle and understanding man, sadly divided the property.

'The younger son soon turned all he had into cash, and

set off for a distant country where he squandered it in wild living. At just about the time his money gave out, a severe famine struck the country and soon he was in dire straits.

'In desperation, he hired himself out to a man who set him to minding the pigs. Many a day he longed to fill his stomach with the pods thrown to the pigs. All his fair-weather friends had deserted him; he had no one to stand by him in his need.

'He came to his senses, and said to himself, "The poorest in my father's employ have food to spare, and here I am, starving to death!"

'Rousing himself to action, he set out for his father's home. He would offer no excuses, no self-justification. He would say, "Father, I've sinned against God and you. I'm no longer worthy to be called your son. Please take me on as one of your hired men!"

'His father, who had been watching for him, saw him when he was still a long way off. His heart went out to him. Running to meet him, he threw his arms around him and kissed him.

'The son started confessing that he had sinned against heaven and his father and could no longer be regarded as a son, but the father silenced him, put his own spotless robe over his tatters, and was soon ordering his servants, "Quick! Bring the finest clothing for my son. Prepare a banquet! This son of mine was dead and has come back to life . . . he was lost and is found." '

The tax collectors and 'sinners' hung on my words, seeing themselves in the prodigal son who was showered with love when he returned to his father. My gaze shifted to the carping spiritual leaders who were muttering ten minutes ago, 'There must be something wrong with the Nazarene, because he welcomes sinners and eats with them.' The next part of my story would be a tactful attempt to reveal them to themselves.

'As the older brother came in from the field, he heard

music and happy laughter. Calling a servant, he asked what was going on.

' "Your brother has come back," the man said, "and your father has a celebration going such as we haven't seen in years!"

' "What!" The older brother exploded in a towering passion and refused to go in.

'The father came and pleaded with him, but he stormed, "I slaved for you all these years! I obeyed all your orders. Yet you never gave me even half a party. This son of yours squanders your property on the scum of the earth, and when he comes home you lay on a sumptuous feast for him!"

' "But, my son, you are always with me and all I have is yours. How could we help celebrating this unforgettable day? This brother of yours — for that is what he is — was dead and now he is alive!" The father's eyes brimmed with tears and his voice choked. "Your brother was lost, and is lost no longer!" '

In the grip of a yearning love for these religious leaders, my enemies, I felt as though I could give my life for them on the spot. In two months' time I would be doing so.

BROUGHT TO LIFE! 57

The man from Martha and Mary of Bethany arrived with the message, 'Lord, the one you love is sick!'

I had already been shown how desperate his condition was. He was dying. 'The end result of this sickness is not death,' I said. 'No, it will result in God's glory. God's Son will be glorified through it.'

The man, seeing I made no move to go to Bethany, was dismayed. 'Lord, aren't you . . . ?' I shook my head and in deep disappointment he set off on his return journey.

I saw that scene in Bethany — shock when the messenger was seen to be alone, then hope as they heard my response: 'The end result of this sickness is not death.' They clung to the words, whispered them urgently into their brother's ears . . . until Lazarus died.

It tested their faith to the utmost. I had said . . . yet he was dead! They could not begin to understand. With the cold body of their dear gentle brother before them, they decided to say no word that might reflect blame on me. In the face of death they would keep on believing. In the face of the apparent failure of my word, their faith would continue! Contemplating this, I was deeply, deeply moved.

During the next two days I sometimes caught a disciple eyeing me strangely. My response to the news of Lazarus's sickness had seemed unnervingly casual. Hadn't I abandoned John the Baptist to death as well, last year? . . .

Then I said to the disciples, 'Let us go back to Judea.'

'Judea!' They were appalled. 'But Rabbi, just recently the Jews there were trying to stone you! Are you sure you want to go back?'

'Are there not twelve hours of daylight?' Meaning, my day of active service is not yet to end in death. 'He who moves about in the daytime does not stumble — he has the light of this world.' All through my daytime I knew exactly what the will of God was, because the Holy Spirit illumined my mind, 'lighted' the way for me as the sun lights up the day. 'It is when a man walks at night that he stumbles, because the light is not in him.' He who walks in a path of his own choosing is in the dark and stumbles.

They could see it was daylight-clear to me that returning to dangerous Judea was God's will.

I went on, 'Our friend Lazarus is asleep. I am going there to wake him up.'

Not realizing that I meant the sleep of death, they said, 'Lord, if he's asleep he's bound to get better.'

'Lazarus is dead. For your sake I am glad I was not there. Now your faith will be boosted. Let us go to him.'

Thomas, not seeing the mighty heavenly angels, said fatalistically, 'Let all of us go, so that we can die with him.'

The distance was less than a day on foot, but I took my time, ministering to the sick and the needy along the way as I customarily did. For the first three days of death the family and friends spent a great deal of time at the grave; but the fourth day saw it mostly deserted.

With my retinue of ecclesiastical spies growing bigger by the day, I arrived at a quiet shady spot near Bethany on the afternoon of the fourth day. In the distance I could hear the wailing from the hired mourners: the artificiality of it jarred on me.

My messenger slipped into the scene of doleful hubbub and whispered a word in Martha's ear. In her customary up-and-doing spirit she was at once on her way, forgetting to tell Mary.

There she was, businesslike in her movements, catching sight of us, faltering in her step, coming more slowly . . . with so much sorrow etched in her face.

'Lord!' Her voice was raw with weeping. 'If only you had been here! My brother would not have died.'

True, but I had felt every pang that went through her heart and Mary's. She saw this in my face, and stumblingly tried to assure me that her faith in me as Son of God had survived her brother's death: 'Even now, Lord, I know God gives you everything you ask.'

What loyalty! I had apparently abandoned her in her hour of need; but, she was saying, I would still be her consolation and hope in the future.

'Your brother will live again,' I said quietly, intending the words for Martha and all Marthas mourning over faithful Lazaruses in years to come.

For a profound minute she stared into my eyes. So that was why I had said the end result of this sickness was not death! I had given my word that Lazarus would rise to life on the day of the resurrection of the just, she concluded.

Believing what she perceived of my assurance, yet with her ache undiminished and her longing unmitigated, she said, 'I know it, Lord. He *will* rise again at the last day.'

Her faith was wonderful, but how I wished it had stretched itself on tiptoe to the words, 'I know it, Lord. *You* will raise him again, at the last day!'

And so, in a moment pregnant with both history and prophecy, I said to her and to my disciples who would soon see me dead, '*I am the Resurrection and the Life!* He who believes in me may die, but he shall come to life! Then, living and believing in me, he shall never ever die. Do you believe this?'

The full meaning of my words escaped her, but one point she saw more clearly than the theologians and teachers of religion in Israel.

'Yes, Lord,' she said. 'I do believe you are the Messiah, the Son of God who was to come into the world.'

It was a fuller confession than I had heard from any of the men whom I considered my apostles; and what made it the more heroic was the tragic background against which it was made.

'Go and fetch Mary,' I suggested.

She went, and did it quietly because she knew of the priestly agitation for my arrest; but my Father overruled her caution. Heaven wanted witnesses of what was about to happen, especially enemy witnesses. Among the mourners were relatives of the family, people of prominence in Jerusalem. All followed Mary, thinking she was rushing off to the grave; and so my contingent of priestly spies was dramatically augmented.

Mary knelt at my feet, choking out the thought she and Martha had been exchanging for four days. 'Oh, Lord, if only you had been here my brother would not have died!' She burst into sobs.

Her heartbroken tears moved me deeply. For long moments my world consisted only of Martha and Mary, as my Father's yearning to comfort them surged through me.

Then the wailing fixed my attention on those around us. By the Holy Spirit I read their hearts. Some were sincere in their grief, even if their expression of it was too extravagant for my taste. Over the others I shuddered. Their grief was pretence, hypocrisy. The conversations they would engage in over the next day or two rang in my ears: there was latent murder in their hearts. They were prominent, respected religionists — but they served Satan.

Righteous indignation swelled in me. I was tempted to unmask them, but my Father's kindness and patience, and Mary's sobbing, caused the words to die on my lips.

'Where have you laid him?' I asked.

Other voices mingled with Martha's 'Come and see, Lord.'

With the ever-growing crowd we came to the burial cave, where there was a renewed outburst of weeping and wailing. Everything blurred before my eyes.

The noise subsided somewhat and I heard exclamations of 'Look at his tears! How he must have loved Lazarus!'

My tears were not for Lazarus. They flowed in sympathy for my friends . . . and in grief because they could weep in the presence of the Life-giver. And because now, and down through the centuries, so many would close the door of life to themselves. Jerusalem's fate was also before me. Their rejection of heaven's light would in a few years lead to a destruction too numbing, too terrible for tears.

Cultured accents could be heard: 'Couldn't this man, who opened the blind man's eyes, have done something to keep Lazarus from dying?' 'If he really works miracles, why was he powerless to do something?'

I groaned and shook my head. There was not a single person here who believed that Lazarus would be brought to life. In the face of all this blindness and doubt, I must press ahead doing what my Father wanted.

'Take away the stone,' I said. I would not command the angels to do it: heaven will not do what men can do.

Martha reached out a hand to check me. 'Lord, no! He's been dead four days! The smell, the stench . . . '

'Martha — didn't you gather from my words that if you have faith you will see the glory of God?'

She dropped her hand, confused. Strong men stepped forward and managed to roll the rock aside, then quickly stepped back as the smell of death struck them. A smothered cry came from Mary, and Martha stood ashen-faced and rigid, swaying slightly.

There he lay, wrapped in strips of linen, with layers of cloth tight over his face. So unconscious, so still in death — he could have been sleeping. Except that if he had been sleeping and not dead to start with, he would have smothered to death in the face cloth; and the smell of decomposing flesh would not have hung heavy on the air.

I stepped closer to the cave. A word of command was all that was needed; but I wanted to focus attention on my loving and all-powerful Father, who worked through me.

Standing there, eyes uplifted, I prayed, 'Father, thank you for hearing me. I know you always hear me, but I am saying this for the benefit of the people standing here, so that they may believe that you sent me.'

Loudly, so that all could hear, I cried, 'Lazarus, come out!'

At once there was no smell of death on the air. The wrapped body stirred, the head twisted, the legs drew up while women shrieked in fright. My command was echoing in that suddenly reconstituted brain. He tried to obey, to sit up, but couldn't, and began to roll in the direction of my voice while the people gasped and staggered back.

I turned, and as they saw the light in my face there were

cries of panic. 'Help him!' I said, pointing to Lazarus. 'Undo the wrappings.'

With trembling hands my disciples freed Lazarus and he stood up strong, vigorous, bright of eye . . . and then flung himself in adoration at my feet.

As shouts of amazement and praise erupted I slipped away as quickly as I could.

WHERE ARE THE NINE? 58

Many who saw Lazarus brought to life put their faith in me. Other Jews at once went to Jerusalem to report to the supreme religious leaders. This resulted in a meeting of the Sanhedrin.

'We decided quite a while ago that limits had to be set to this fellow's activities,' a prominent Pharisee said. 'And what have we achieved? Nothing! By some power that the devil gives him, he goes about performing miracles that will soon have everybody eating out of his hand. Then the Romans will come and sweep away our temple and our nation!'

Caiaphas, high priest for about thirteen years already, barked, 'Words, words!' He was furious. As a Sadducee he believed there was no resurrection from death. What I had just done disproved this. To give up his false doctrine never occurred to him; to hate me for showing up its falseness was now a seething passion with him. 'We need deeds! Can't you see it is better for one man to die for the people than for a whole nation to perish?'

Which was incongruously prophetic, seeing that the Son of Man had to die so that millions of sinners throughout history could live.

As the eminent religious leaders plotted to take my life, I withdrew to the Judean village Ephraim, near the Jordan valley wilderness. After a time I went north to the borders of Galilee — a circuitous journey that would end in Jerusalem — and came across ten lepers.

'Jesus, Master, have pity on us!' they called, keeping their distance as the law required.

Nine were Jews and one a Samaritan. I could cure them with a word, but that would not help them spiritually. They would have to exercise faith in God and in my word, not for a moment but for days.

'Go and show yourselves to the priests,' I said.

They stared at me, then glanced at their hands and feet. They were still full of leprosy. Showing themselves to the priests at the temple was an application to be officially declared cured . . . but they were not cured!

'Does he mean . . . we'll be healed on the way?' one asked tremulously.

I was going into the nearby village and they could not follow. Wrestling with their uncertainties, they tried to assess their position by recalling all they had heard about me. 'Son of God . . . healer of blind people and paralytics and lepers . . . brought to life a man name Lazarus. Right here at Nain, brought a widow's son back to life . . . .'

They decided to obey my word, and every day as they scavenged their way down towards Jerusalem rehearsed stories about me, and every night fell asleep still leprous. Then one morning they saw Jerusalem's skyline, and burst out in shouting as they found all trace of the leprosy gone.

Had they remained with me, they would have died in their leprosy. An obedient, persevering faith had made the difference.

And so ten men presented themselves to my priestly enemies, were declared cured of leprosy, and then told the priests how the cure had come about. They were ten letters from me to the temple authorities, conveying this message:

'I am continuing with my Father's work. Here are ten of my innumerable credentials, undeniably authentic. And you see, I do respect the temple and God's laws concerning it: I sent these men to you as the law requires.'

Some of the priests felt strange tugs at their hearts; others seethed with anger because they could not escape my preaching even at a distance.

Nine of the healed lepers went home to resume a normal life. One — the Samaritan — walked the length of Judea until he found me, and threw himself at my feet in an expression of passionate gratitude.

'Were all ten not healed?' I asked. 'What happened to the other nine? Was none moved by gratitude to come and give praise to God, except one man — and he a foreigner?'

To him I said, 'Stand up, live a normal life. Your faith has made you well.'

THE UNJUST JUDGE   59

As we moved eastward towards the Jordan, there to turn south on the last leg of the journey that would within four weeks take me to the cross in Jerusalem, I continued serving people and teaching.

A subject that came up again was prayer. To me the greatest principle in prayer, as in all life, is my Father's will. This *is* my prayer, my life. But another principle is perseverance, otherwise man's will never merges with God's. To focus on never losing heart in prayer, I told this parable:

'A widow kept coming to a judge for justice against her opponent. The judge, who couldn't be bothered with God or man, at first refused her, but then thought, "If I don't see that she gets justice, she'll nag me to death! I'd better help her."

'There is a lesson in this. Will the good God not vindicate his chosen ones who cry to him day and night? He most certainly will! Yet . . . when the Son of Man comes, will he find faith on the earth? . . . '

One day the Pharisees brought up the question of divorce: 'Is it lawful for a man to divorce his wife for any and every reason?'

'Have you never read in the Scriptures that God at the beginning made them male and female — complementary? That is why a man will leave his father and mother and be united with his wife, the two becoming "one flesh". They are no longer two, but one — not separate, but united. What God has joined together, man must not separate.'

'Then why did Moses decree that a man could divorce his wife by note of dismissal?' They were eager to put me at odds with the revered Moses.

'Moses made the concession in view of your heartless attitude.' They knew what I meant: the wives were chattels, and what Moses did had the effect of improving their lot. 'But that was not God's original principle. Anyone who divorces his wife, except for marital unfaithfulness, and remarries, commits adultery.'

Later my disciples commented, 'If the situation between husband and wife is so stringent, it is better not to marry!'

'Your suggestion will not work for most people. Some, of course, are by birth incapable of marriage. Others are turned into eunuchs by men. And some renounce marriage with a spiritual objective.' The sect of the Essenes rejected marriage. But I instituted marriage in the beginning, saying that it was not good for a man to be alone; and some of my disciples — like Peter — were married men. Standing for the higher ideal, the original principle as I propounded it to the Pharisees, I concluded, 'Let the one who can accept it' — my teaching — 'accept it'.

My disciples still sometimes acted in ways betraying ignorance of me. In Israel it was usual for children to be taken to a rabbi so that he could lay his hands in blessing on them. When some mothers brought their children to me for my blessing, I waited to see what my disciples would do.

'No, no, no!' they said to the mothers. 'Don't bother the master with things like that!'

I intervened. 'Let the children come to me. Don't try to stop them. The kingdom of heaven belongs to such as these!'

I laid my hands on the bigger children, took the little ones in my arms, blessed them all, and sent the mothers home with a sense of the nearness of heaven.

I was walking on when an expensively dressed young man, deeply impressed with the love shown the children, ran after me, kneeled and asked with obvious sincerity and earnestness, 'Good teacher, what good thing must I do to get eternal life?'

'Good?' I echoed. 'Why call me good? There is only One who is good.'

I waited for him to respond. Would he say: Yes, only God — but you are the Son of God? Would he acknowledge me as more than teacher or prophet — as the Messiah?

His faith fell short; he waited in silence for me to speak.

I said, 'If you want eternal life to open to you, keep the commandments.'

The crowd pressed in about us, listening. The young man blinked uncomfortably. I was telling him he must obey the commandments of God if he wanted eternal life; this implied that he was not doing so! 'Which commandments?' he hedged, looking for a way of escape.

I quoted from my handwriting, the Ten Commandments, concentrating on those commands applying the principle of love to one's fellow man . . . here lay his weakness.

'All those I have kept,' he said in his self-deception. After citing the commandments against murder, unchastity, stealing, lying, and disrespect for parents, I had deliberately summed up the second table of the moral law with the words, 'Love your neighbour as yourself' — because his life was one of self-centredness, selfishness.

'What do I still lack?' he asked.

He wanted reassurance, a touch from my hand, the

blessing I had given the children. Anything, so long as it involved no change of character in himself; and preferably something effortless.

I gazed into his eyes, and loved him. He was sincerely religious, upright, clean-living; and honest enough to know that he still fell short. I knew exactly what he needed: a true love for God. With all his exemplary religion, he did not have it. The love of God would bring devotion of heart, heart religion. It would give him a clear view of his true spiritual state; then would come humility and repentance, a hiding of himself in God's grace.

What he needed could not be had on the cheap. 'If you want to go the whole way, go, sell your possessions and give the proceeds to the poor, and you will have treasure in heaven. Then come and follow me.'

I was offering him what I had offered Matthew . . . and Matthew left his money tables, his business and everything. Soon Judas Iscariot would be gone, an apostleship vacant. This brilliant young man of position, personality, sincerity, could be my co-worker, a divine force among men. But he must first give me all there was of him; and the test would be his wealth.

My son, give me your heart, I pleaded with him silently. What I ask seems severe, but I have read your character. I am asking you to give up what is subtly corrupting your soul, becoming an idol in your life. Oh, give it up and live! Trust me; give up your own ideas of what is best for you. Surrender yourself, and I guarantee you will find yourself!

He slowly rose from his knees, blinking uncertainly. His moment of salvation had come . . . and gone.

'Well . . . ' he said sadly, shifting his weight to his other foot. No longer meeting my eye, he began to sidle away, while my heart groaned and threatened to break. The Pharisees — influential, esteemed above all others — believed that prosperity and wealth were proof of God's approval. The idea was pervasive: even my disciples were infected with it. And Judas Iscariot, one of my twelve, was so obsessed with money that he would soon sell me to my enemies.

With my eyes on the retreating back of the rich young ruler, I said to my disciples, 'I tell you the truth: it is hard for a rich man to enter the kingdom of heaven.' I looked at Judas. 'To put it more strongly, it is easier for a camel to go through the eye of a needle than for a rich man to enter the kingdom of God!'

They started in amazement. I was talking about an utter impossibility; and I meant it. But I was thinking less of money than of spirit, attitude, character. What I was saying applied to rich and poor alike . . . although the temptations are stronger and more numerous for the rich.

Oh, that Judas would change his attitude towards wealth! To his materialism, the rich young ruler had made a sensible decision. He could not see that the man had exchanged life for death.

'But Lord . . . in that case . . . if the heaven-blessed people are not saved — who *can* be?' the disciples gasped.

Can avarice and materialism, I asked myself, be overcome? 'In human strength this is impossible,' I said. 'But in God's power anything is possible' — even transformation of character, the supreme 'impossibility'.

Peter, as though to prove that a mercenary spirit had not passed him by, said, 'We've left everything to become your followers: *what's in it for us?*'

'What's in it for *me?*' Oh, how my heart wrenched! I gazed into the face of this poor, weak, amiable man who would soon be denying with cursing that he ever knew me, and prayed silently for him.

'Let me assure you, my disciples, of this. When the earth is renewed and the Son of Man mounts his glorious throne, you who have followed me will sit enthroned to judge the twelve tribes of Israel.' This is what you can look forward to. You will share my glory and endless life.

But even in this temporary life you will benefit. You

may lose your wife or brother or home for my sake. I cannot promise you a hundred wives, brothers or houses in return — not literally. Figuratively, yes! I can assure you that many homes will open to you, many believing families will take you to their bosom. You will have 'a hundred' families of loved ones, 'a hundred' houses 'will be yours'.

'Anyone who has left home and hearth, property or loved ones, for my sake, will be compensated a hundred times over in this life — with persecutions! — and receive eternal life. But . . . ' — the rich young ruler; the leaders of Israel; the priests, theologians; Israel as opposed to the Gentiles; the shallowness of judging by appearance and impressions and tradition — 'many who are first will be last, and many who are last will be first!'

I wanted to make plain that divine approval is never earned — not even by leaving everything to be my follower. Christ's people do not strike a bargain with God. Everything is by grace; and God looks for a willing spirit, and faithfulness. So I told them a story.

'The kingdom of heaven works on this principle. A landowner hired men early in the morning to work in his vineyard, agreeing to pay them the usual day's wage. Three hours later he hired more men, who left the matter of reward to him. Another three hours and he did the same thing. An hour before sunset he came across more men who had never been hired, and they went to work for him without asking about payment.

'At sunset the workers filed past. He paid the one-hour men the full day's wage. The full-day men saw this and, thinking they deserved a lot more than the one-hour men, expected a much higher reward. But he gave them the full day's wage, nothing more!

'When they protested he said, "Am I not keeping to my agreement with you? And weren't those other men willing and faithful? Moreover, *they* never tried to bargain with me over what they deserved!" '

I looked at Peter, my what's-in-it-for-me disciple, and warned, 'So the last will be first, and the first last!'

And in one sense all the saved will be on an equal footing — having eternal, glorious, happy life in God's presence.

BARTIMAEUS AND ZACCHAEUS

A mass of people, alerted by the pilgrims who had gone ahead, was waiting for us near Jericho. As we moved towards the city gate I tried in vain to catch a glimpse through the crowd of the two blind beggars shown me by the Spirit.

Then I did fleetingly see them, abjectly begging, puzzled at the presence of so many people. Just inside the gate I stopped, bringing my entourage to a halt. Some minutes passed. The beggars were getting answers to their questions. I was giving faith a chance to come to life.

I turned round and left the city, the crowd swirling noisily about me, mystified that I had reversed direction.

One of the blind men, Bartimaeus, was shouting, 'Jesus, Lord, have mercy on me!'

His voice was lost in the general excitement. I walked on. Now both men were screaming in unison, 'Jesus, Son of David, have mercy on us!'

The Messianic title 'Son of David' . . . . Men were telling them to be quiet, to stop bothering me with their begging for money. But there was no thought of money with them.

I was going on, passing out of their lives. 'Son of David! Have mercy on us!'

I stopped and looked steadily in their direction until the crush of men and women opened and it was seen, to surprise all around, that my attention was fixed on two scruffy beggars.

'Let them come,' I said.

The crowd was silent, all eyes. 'Come, he's calling for you!' voices urged.

Bartimaeus shot forward, out of his cloak. Men shrank back from his groping hands. He came to an instinctive halt in front of me, panting, eyes lifeless and empty.

'What do you want me to do for you?'

'Lord, I want my sight back!' Bartimaeus gasped.

The other man was led forward and with vacant stare stood nodding some distance behind Bartimaeus, quiet, unobtrusive.

For three reasons I wanted to work this miracle. First — love for these suffering beggars. Second, to help the faith of the throng of pilgrims survive my death in two weeks' time. Third, to inspire confidence in future generations even when heaven seems to be passing by their cries for help.

I stepped between the men so that I could touch their eyes simultaneously. 'Have back your sight! Your faith has made you well!'

How those dull eyes flooded with light!

'Go,' I said, turning on my heel to go back into Jericho; but the two men, unable to tear themselves away, followed me . . . .

We made our slow way along the cramped street in a westerly direction, my thoughts not so much on the press of people as on a little man trying breathlessly to get a glimpse past a forest of backs and shoulders. My heart sang in me as I read the story of his life.

Zacchaeus was that rare person — one with a heart open to divine influences. For a while he seemed just another Jew acquiring wealth hand over fist as an unscrupulous chief tax collector for the Romans. But he was reading the Scriptures and coming under conviction of his wrongdoing.

Desperate for a glimpse of the Man of Galilee about

whom he had been hearing so much, he now ran ahead to the outskirts of the town, found a sycamore-fig tree whose wide branches stretched across the street, and climbed it.

He thought of his pressing business appointments, with so many pilgrims passing through to Jerusalem, then dismissed them from his mind. His main worry now was whether I would come this way. His hands shook with his feverish desire to see me, hear a word from my lips, and give his whole life to God.

There he was, incongruously well-dressed for someone crouching in a tree, eyes wide, scanning the throng below, heart beating uncontrollably. I stopped below him.

'Zacchaeus!' He froze on his branch and the crowd stopped in midstride. 'Zacchaeus, hurry down! I must be your guest today!'

It was the first time I had ever invited myself to someone's home. He tumbled dishevelled from his tree, overwhelmed and speechless.

As in a dream he led the way to his rich man's home where I was to open heavenly truth to his mind. We were about to go in when the priests and rabbis started a chorus of protest.

'Look at that! Guest in a *sinner's* home! This is a disgrace! Scandalous!'

The little man swung round, seeming to grow a hand's breadth as he faced my accusers.

'I take you all to witness! Lord, here and now I undertake to give half my possessions to charity! Where I have overtaxed anyone, I am ready to repay him four times over!'

He trembled in the grip of holy emotion, of high resolve to do twice as much as God or man could expect.

To him, my enemies and the throng, I said, 'Salvation has come to this house today! This man is a true son of Abraham!'

By God's grace that turned impossibilities into possibilities here was a rich man who had entered the kingdom of grace. Oh, how much the rich young ruler had lost by sadly turning away!

Saying, 'The Son of Man has come to seek and save what is lost,' I went into the home of the despised family.

BETRAYAL 61

There was a popular movement in Galilee a year earlier to crown me King, after the feeding of the thousands with five loaves and two tiny fish, so that I had to escape into the hills. Now, with my disciples encouraging this same sentiment behind my back — and a liberation mentality rife in Israel — I was under great pressure.

Ahead of us was Jerusalem and the Passover Feast, commemorating Israel's birth as a nation with the deliverance from Egypt so many centuries ago. How fitting that the miracle-working Messiah should now take the throne and drive the Roman forces into the sea! The masses of Israel were like a great heaving ocean, ready to send a tidal wave across the land. All they needed was my word, and a million roaring, shrilling people would carry me up to the temple, sweeping the religious leaders aside and crowning me.

Nothing I had said could avert the frenzy building up; but I must keep trying. In retrospect some would understand and take heart.

There was a man of noble birth, I told the crowds, who went on a long journey to a distant country to be crowned as king, after which he would return.

Noble birth — my descent from King David. Crowned — the throne of David. They were making correct deductions, I saw — but the long journey to a distant country? They were disquieted . . . what did I mean? Was I going away? And for a long time, as I implied?

Now, how were his ten servants to serve him while he was gone on his long journey to the distant place? To each he gave one mina, about one hundred days' wages, telling them to trade with the money until he came back.

While he was gone his subjects rejected him — virtually the whole nation. At last he came back and had an accounting with his servants. By devoted sensible work one had added to his mina another ten; another had got five more; but one had simply wrapped his money in a piece of cloth and kept it safe.

'You with the ten will take charge of ten cities. You with the five get five cities. But you who could not even produce interest on your mina will have it taken from you. Hand it to the man with ten minas! And as for the people who rejected me as their king, bring them here to lose their lives!'

I left a somewhat subdued crowd to ponder this parable.

A superficial observer might have thought no prominent person in Israel believed in me; but this was not so. Rabbi Nicodemus, influential and wealthy, had shielded me so tellingly in the Sanhedrin that crucial councils were now called without notifying him. Joseph of Arimathea was a council member who stood ready to support me with his wealth. Other leading men openly called themselves disciples of mine.

One of these was Simon, a Pharisee whom I had cured of leprosy. Just six days before my death, on Saturday evening, soon after sunset had brought the close of the Sabbath and ushered in the first day of the week, I was guest of honour at a dinner in his home at Bethany. Simon was on my right and Lazarus on my left.

The evening wore on with a pleasant hubbub of conversation. Martha served the guests, and an apparently endless stream of people drifted in to stare at her brother, the man who had been dead for four days. Some had a word with him, eager to know what it was like to be dead, hoping for fantastic ghostly impressions; and I smiled, knowing that they were looking for rain where there were no clouds.

Lazarus's invariable vibrant response, 'What I know is

this: the one who brought me back to life two months ago when I was already decomposing is the Son of God, the promised Messiah!' was bringing conviction to one after another of those who talked with him.

I became preoccupied with what was happening behind me. When Mary first heard me speaking about my coming death, she was shattered. Then she decided to spend her savings on the best perfume money could buy, to anoint my body after my death. Now everybody she knew was saying I would within days be crowned King . . . and the dear child of God, overwhelmed with relief and joy, as well as with gratitude for what I had done for her, wanted to be first to pay me homage.

She had the precious alabaster bottle in her trembling hands. Past the outstretched feet of the reclining Simon she came. Breaking the bottle open she stood looking at the back of my head, an infinity of love in her heart. The tears began to course down her face. I felt them on my feet. Lying propped on my left elbow I did not move . . . she was trying to be unobserved.

Stepping over my sandals she was now pouring a liberal amount of her costly oil of nard on my head — I was the anointed King of her life. Simon stopped talking, glanced sharply sideways. Then she was at my feet, emptying her bottle over them, shaking with her silent sobs, bending low to wipe my feet with her hair and kiss them.

As the perfume filled the room everyone looked up. In the silence Judas Iscariot's intake of breath and whisper could be heard: 'What waste is this? It could have been sold for a year's wages and the money given to the poor!'

Others looked shocked, nodded, grunted a word or two in agreement . . . and Mary, hearing, shrank back in an agony of dismay.

'The money given to the poor,' I thought. You say that, when you as our treasurer have been pilfering money from our bag? You wanted that money also within reach of your long fingers?

I could unmask him with a word, but this was not in my nature. And if I humiliated him this would be urged as a reason why he betrayed me; he would gain sympathy from millions of unsanctified minds in years to come.

Looking at Judas but speaking to all in the room, I said, 'Why embarrass the girl? What she did to me is something beautiful. You will never be without the poor among you — but you will not always have me.'

I glanced from face to face. They did not understand; clearer words were needed. 'By pouring this fragrant oil over my body she was in effect preparing me for my . . . funeral.'

Beyond my death I saw the religion I had founded being carried through the marching years to the ends of the earth, and said, 'I assure you, wherever this gospel is proclaimed in all the world, what she has done will be told in memory of her.'

A quick glance round. Mary was sitting on the floor, her fingers touching my feet, blinking away her tears, radiantly happy . . . that word 'funeral' had not got through to her.

Judas now knew, from my look and his own guilty intuition, that I knew of his stealing, that I had no illusions about his character. He felt the indirect rebuke in my commendation of Mary, and could hardly wait for the dinner to end so that his anger could explode into the night.

And Simon . . . poor Simon. Churning in his mind was the thought, 'I'm glad I didn't accept him as Messiah! Why, he's not even the prophet I took him to be! Otherwise he'd have known of her past. If he knew what I know about her, he'd never have let her touch him!'

Really, Simon? Do you think because I shrink from the touch of sin I recoil also from the touch of sinners? And how is it that you — yes, *you*, whose leprosy went beyond that of the body — are such an expert on Mary? Do you think I don't know the circumstances that caused her to flee to

Magdala, where I met her and finally freed her from the chaos of her mind and life?

'Simon, I have something to say to you,' I said.

'Yes, Master?'

'Two men owed money. One owed the equivalent of wages for five hundred days, the other for fifty days. Both were in a hopeless position — they could pay back nothing. So the moneylender acquitted both of their debt. Now which will love him most?'

For a moment he could not see where my words were leading. 'Why, the one who had the bigger debt remitted.'

'Yes.' I turned to Mary. 'Do you see this girl? I came into your house and you provided no water for my feet, but she splashed her tears on my feet and dried them with her hair. You gave me no kiss, but she has hardly stopped kissing my feet. You put no common oil on my head, but she poured perfumed oil on my feet. So I tell you, her multiple sins have been forgiven . . . you see the evidence, her great love. Where little has been forgiven, little love is shown.'

To her I said, 'Your sins are all forgiven.'

Some of Simon's guests grumbled below their breath, 'Who is this, to forgive sins even?' But Simon was abashed and said nothing, confronted with his own guilt and plunged into a worry that held promise for his future.

'Your faith has saved you,' I said to her. 'Go in peace . . . .'

Judas found the priests and Pharisees in council, anxiously saying to one another, 'Will he come to the Feast or once more evade us? If he does come we'll have to be very careful — we don't want a riot among the people!'

'What are you willing to pay me if I hand him over to you?' he demanded.

Astonished and delighted, they counted out thirty silver pieces for him, and he went off to watch for a chance to betray me.

The Sanhedrin decided, 'All these reports we are getting of people, even priests, joining this Galilean because of the testimony of that man Lazarus can mean only one thing: Lazarus will also have to die. If we don't get rid of him, our people will keep on being led astray.'

TRIUMPHAL ENTRY 62

Up to now I had discouraged every effort to treat me like a King. For once this would change. Before the week was out the religious leaders would arrest me in secret, try and condemn me at dead of night, and do their utmost to have me dead before the masses of Israel could wake up to what was happening. Now, before the final rush of events, I must take the best part of a million people to witness that I was their Lord and King. Then, when the blow fell, the honest among them would be led to study the prophecies of Scripture and discover that I had fulfilled the Messianic predictions.

One of these prophecies was that made by Zechariah five hundred years ago when he exhorted Jerusalem to burst out in shouting and rejoicing, for 'lo, your King is coming to you, with righteousness and salvation, in humility and riding on an ass's colt'.

Any man could, of course, ride into Jerusalem on a donkey and claim to have fulfilled Zechariah's prophecy. But his claim would not be true. To fulfil the prophecy he would need to have demonstrated lifelong righteousness of character; he would have to give his life for sinners so that he could offer them salvation; all Jerusalem must turn out to hail him as King . . . and in his humility there must be no room for a worldly kingship.

To set the seal of divinity even on the procuring of the donkey, I sent two disciples to the village of Bethphage. 'As you enter it you will find a house where the road curves.

At its front door there will be a donkey tethered. Beside her will be her foal, which no one has ever ridden. Untie them and bring them here. If anyone challenges you, say this: The Lord needs them. He will at once let you take them.'

They went off in a thoughtful mood — I had for the first time referred to myself as Lord. Finding everything just as I had seen in vision, they were challenged, answered as directed, and were struck with wonder when the owners, utter strangers, at once acknowledged my right as King to commandeer their property.

Since last night at the dinner in Simon's house, Lazarus had hardly left my side. It was now late morning and a crowd of Passover pilgrims had gathered to inspect his grave, talk to eyewitnesses of his restoration to life, and follow us in awe as we headed for Jerusalem.

A commotion was set off by the arrival of the donkeys. The ancient Jewish custom of a royal entry into the city on a donkey! I was at last willing to be crowned as King!

Beside themselves with excitement, the disciples spread their cloaks on the colt and carpeted the road with them as I mounted and started off. The people cheered — an explosion of sound. From everywhere they came with olive branches, palm branches, and their outer garments to cover the road. They had no banners, but hundreds waving palm branches fell in ahead of me, singing and shouting.

'Our Messiah! Our King!' they cheered; and for the first time I accepted their homage.

The countryside was alive with figures scurrying towards us, and some were rushing off pell-mell to bring the news to Jerusalem. By the minute we grew more massive, were forced to crawl more slowly. After a while there was nothing to be seen in any direction but heads, arms, palm branches.

At last I could make out the crest of the Hill of Olives; and then it disappeared under a tide of humanity. The people of Jerusalem were joining us. From hill to hill the roar echoed: 'Hosanna to the Son of David! Blessed is he who comes in the name of the Lord! Hosanna in the highest!'

Priests and rabbis had also come pouring out of Jerusalem and were vainly screaming themselves hoarse to silence the people. They caught up with me at the brow of Olivet.

'Teacher! Rebuke your disciples! Silence them!'

The priests at the temple had sounded the trumpet for 'evening' service: it was three o'clock. Few responded, virtually all the city being with me; and this lashed to fever pitch the envy and fury of these men.

'Let me tell you this,' I replied. 'If they were to keep quiet, the very stones would shout aloud.' You cannot silence God.

While hundreds began to chant the words of Zechariah about the King coming to Jerusalem, I stared down at Jerusalem and the beautiful white-and-gold temple. If these people were true and faithful to God, all that the prophets foretold about this city's world-wide greatness would come true. But, alas, here was a city that killed its prophets, rejected its Redeemer and wished to silence God's voice whenever it sounded an unwelcome note. Precious souls were choosing death.

The pain of it shook me, and those who saw my tears fell silent, amazed.

'Jerusalem, if only you knew what could bring you peace! You are so blind! The days will come when your enemies will set up siege works, encircle you, choke the life out of you. You and your children will suffer and not one stone will remain on another, because you did not discern the time of God's coming to you!'

Leaders from the Sanhedrin toiled up the hill, demanding, 'Who is this? What's going on?'

My disciples, inspired by a wisdom greater than their own, quoted to them the prophecies about the Messiah; but they turned to the Roman soldiers who had hurried to the scene and futilely denounced me as leader of a rebellion.

I sat praying for this nation; it was not yet too late for them. For more than two hours I made no move — it was time to moderate the ardour of the people.

They rested from their shouting, debated the coming enthronement of their King who would free them from the foreign yoke, conjectured about the political and military strategy I would follow, and time and again burst into song.

Then, as the leaders of Israel were haranguing them and the sun began to set, I quietly slipped down into the valley and up to the Sheep Gate, noticed and followed by few.

Here a crowd had been waiting for hours. They went wild with excitement, bringing a thunder of sudden realization from the great concourse of people on Olivet.

Leaving the colt in the care of others, I strode down the cramped street on my left, visited the temple that meant infinitely more to me than it did to Israel and its spiritual leaders, and left for Bethany by another gate.

The multitude came to crown me as their King but could not find me.

Divine prophecy had been fulfilled. Every mind was now focused on the Lamb of God who had come through the Sheep Gate, so that the coming Friday's sacrifice could be better understood. And, dimly and in miniature, I had given a foreshadowing of my coming in the clouds of heaven with power and glory, amid the triumph of angels and the rejoicing of the men and women who belonged to God.

THE KINGDOM TAKEN AWAY   63

After spending the night in prayer I was on my way to Jerusalem early Monday morning. Passing an orchard of as yet leafless fig trees, I stopped at the sight of one tree so luxuriantly leafed out that one could not but expect fruit on it.

'How hungry I am for some fruit, even if it isn't fully ripe,' I said to the disciples, and we went to the tree.

There was nothing but leaves — exactly like Israel, I thought. A show and form of godliness, but no fruit of godliness. Ceremonies and traditions intermixed with heavenly truth; and little heart-religion, little real contact with God.

Tomorrow the religious leaders would finally reject me. For the sake of all my followers, now and in years to come, I would use this fig tree in an acted parable. Tomorrow I would say to Israel, 'Your house is left to you desolate'; and this tree would eventually be an unforgettable lesson to all who love me.

Addressing the tree, I said, 'May no one ever again eat fruit from you!'

Astonished at my unaccustomed behaviour, the disciples followed me into Jerusalem.

The temple was in a worse state than when I cleansed it three years earlier, its outer court like a vast cattle yard with buying, selling, shrill bargaining — all part of the fig leaves rattling in the wind, with no fruit of sin-repentance and obedience of life.

Mounting some steps, I swept my eyes over the desecrated court. The noise died down, became a deep silence. The divinity seen on the mountain of transfiguration was in full evidence.

'It is written,' I said, my voice echoing back from the walls, ' "My house will be called a house of prayer," but you are making it a "den of robbers". Take these things away!'

I had not allowed the masses to crown me King; but I would now act with kingly authority, as guardian of the temple. Stepping down, I began to overturn the tables full of money, doves, cereal, salt, incense and oil. Priests who vowed three years ago never again to flee from me, scampered away in fear. Within minutes the place was clear of animals, traders, priests and temple officials.

I was in full charge, and would show the true business of the temple. Among the pilgrims who had remained, and those now pouring in from the street, were many who were blind, deaf, crippled or sick. I spoke gently to them and healed all of them. Children began to appear with palm branches which they waved as they shouted yesterday's hosannas: 'Blessed is he who comes in the name of the Lord!' and 'Behold, your King comes to you with righteousness and salvation!'

When panic abated the religious leaders drifted back, saw, heard, felt righteously indignant and tried to silence the voices, to no avail.

'Do you hear what these children are saying?' they appealed to me almost frantically.

'I do. Have you never read the Scripture, "You have made children and infants your praise"?'

They were unable to accomplish any further temple business that day; the temple was a place of quiet worship, holy joy, salvation . . . serving man's need, not his greed.

Overnight, Bethany. Tuesday morning, the exclamations of the disciples as they saw the fig tree withered. Peter: 'Rabbi, look! The fig tree you cursed is dead from the roots up!'

Later they would know that the leafless fig trees represented the Gentile nations, whose time for leaf and fruit lay ahead; and the withered tree which had been so glorious with promise was Israel.

My disciples would encounter mountainous obstacles as they carried out my Gospel commission; so now I reminded them, 'Have faith in God. If, moved by God, you tell this mountain in unwavering faith to throw itself into the sea, it will happen.'

They had seen me move many a mountain — as in the cleansing of the temple yesterday. Where the heart was cleansed — of grudges, worldliness, a spirit of self — God would, as you serve his will in prayer, flatten every mountain in your way.

While we were talking about a withered tree and faith, the Sanhedrin was in session. 'When he had the nerve to impose his authority on the temple three years ago we asked him for a miraculous sign of his authority.' 'Well, he has since then healed the blind, dumb, leprous. He's walked on the sea, fed thousands miraculously, supposedly brought the dead to life. Let's not ask him for signs and miracles — that's his strong point. So what do we do?' 'Ask for his authority. Who authorized him? We never did. Get him to admit before witnesses that he had no permission, no authority!'

I was preaching and teaching in the temple. A whole committee came, impressive, important, priests and theologians. The crowd was awed.

'By what authority do you do these things? And who gave it to you?' Rich garments, tiara on his head, majestic bearing, flowing silvered beard and hair.

'When you answer my question I will answer yours. John's baptism: where did it come from? Heaven — or men?'

They retired to discuss it. 'If we say from heaven, which I'm afraid is the way some of us lean, he'll want to know why we never accepted him as a prophet. Then we're in a trap, because John called this Nazarene the Messiah — so why do we reject *that?* On the other hand, if we say it was all on a human level, the people are capable of stoning us — they're all for John as a prophet!'

They came back and the crowd held its breath. 'We don't know.'

'Then you prove yourselves incompetent to assess credentials and authority, and there is no point in my telling you about my authority.' I spoke softly, soberly, because I did not want to humiliate them.

They retired a few paces, stiffly, grimly, bewildered and raging inwardly.

'Tell me what you think of this. A man had two sons and said to the first, "Go and work today in the vineyard." "I won't," he said, but later changed his mind and went.

'He said the same to the second, who responded with an "I will, sir," but never went. Now, which of the two was more satisfactory to the father?'

The crowd waited till the priests and theologians were forced to admit, 'The first.'

'Let me tell you, those you regard as pariahs are entering God's kingdom ahead of you! John came to show you the way of righteousness and you did not believe him. The pariahs did! And after all you have seen since then, you still refuse to repent and believe John's testimony.'

I felt a pang of sorrow. In God's sight there are just two classes: those who obey him and those who do not. Won't you admit that to yourselves?

'Listen to this story. A landowner planted a vineyard, protected it with a wall, dug a winepress in it, and built a watchtower. Then he leased it to some farmers and went abroad. When the harvest time approached he sent his servants to the tenants to collect his share of the crop.

'The tenants seized his servants, assaulted one, killed another, stoned a third. He sent more servants, who suffered the same fate. Last of all he sent his son, sure they would respect him. But they said, "Let's kill the heir and take his inheritance!" They dragged him out of the vineyard and killed him. Now, dear friends, what will the landowner, when he comes, do to those tenants?'

I was speaking to the whole crowd, but they looked at the Sanhedrin men, who for a moment felt on sufficiently safe ground. Their spokesman answered, 'Obviously, those men are wretches who deserve a wretched end. He will lease the vineyard to other tenants, more faithful ones.'

I gazed at him sadly until he and his friends

remembered their attempts to kill me, remembered the money they had already paid Judas to betray me. Now they knew what I meant: God was the landowner, Israel the vineyard, the protecting wall the divine law, the tower the temple, the servants the prophets, and the Son of God stood before them. They were mortified in the extreme for having just pronounced sentence on themselves.

Pityingly I said, 'Have you never read in the Scripture: "The stone which the builders rejected has become the key cornerstone. This is the Lord's doing and to us it is wonderful"?

'So I must tell you, the kingdom of God will be taken away from you and given to a people who will produce the proper fruit. He who falls on this stone will be broken to pieces; those on whom it falls will be crushed.'

Many — even some of the priests — were coming to a deep conviction. But most of the religious leaders would have arrested me then and there were it not for the crowd.

THOSE WHO LOVE THEIR LIFE   64

The priests and doctors of religion still lingered within reach of my voice, hoping for a word that they could use against me. Although unworried by the menace they represented, I was deeply concerned for their spiritual needs. And for believers in general, because so *few* feel a need for a transformation of character, so *few* see the need to become like their Father in heaven.

This need I now presented in the form of a parable.

'The kingdom of heaven is like this. A king prepared a feast for his son's wedding, but when his messengers summoned the invited guests, they would not come. He sent others to appeal to them, urge them, give them a second chance; but they were either too preoccupied with business and social matters, or else assaulted and even killed the messengers. Furious, the king sent troops to kill them and burn down their city. Then he sent his servants into the streets to gather guests for his feast.

'When he entered the banquet hall he found a man without the prescribed wedding clothes and asked, "Friend, how did you get in here without wedding clothes?" The man had no excuse, and the king ordered his attendants, "Tie him up and throw him out into the darkness, where men weep and gnash their teeth in self-reproach."

'You see, many are invited, but *few* put on the wedding garment.'

My Father stands ready to *impute* his righteousness to them, then to *impart* it to them — but they must fulfil the conditions.

The religious dignitaries left and I went on teaching. Eventually another group arrived, younger men, very purposeful in pushing their way through the crowd. They started with flattery and a show of honesty.

'Teacher, we know you as a man of integrity who is never swayed from saying plainly what is right or wrong. What do you say on this: Is it right to pay taxes to Caesar, or not?'

They were Herodians and Pharisees, sworn enemies of one another — yet united against me! . . . If I said no, the supporters of King Herod would lay a charge of sedition against me. If I said yes, all Israel would consider me a traitor to the Jewish cause.

'You hypocrites! Why are you laying a trap for me? Show me the money in which the tax is paid.'

They handed me a silver coin. 'Whose head is this depicted on the coin, and whose inscription?'

'Caesar's.'

'Give to Caesar what is Caesar's, and to God what is God's.'

This was turning into a long Tuesday of spies and

traps. The Sadducees, scorning all thought of a return from death, came a bit later with an artful question.

'Teacher, Moses said if a man dies childless, his brother must marry his widow and raise a family for him. Now, we knew of seven brothers. The first married, died childless and left his wife to number two. The same thing happened successively to the other brothers, right down to the seventh. Last of all the woman died. At the resurrection whose wife will she be, since all seven were married to her?'

I said, 'Your assumptions are incorrect — because your understanding of the Scriptures is unreliable, as is your grasp of God's infinity. As the angels in heaven do not give birth to children, so at the resurrection there will be no need for marriage among humans.

'As for resurrection from death — have you never read what God himself said to you: "I am the God of Abraham, the God of Isaac, and the God of Jacob"? He is not the God of the dead but of the living.'

At the time God spoke those words to Moses, the three were dead . . . and what honour is there in being the God of permanently dead men? But in the resurrection God would raise them to life. This makes him the God of the living!

A Pharisee theologian, seeing the Sadducees silenced, was prompted by spies to come forward with a question that might, it was hoped, lead me to say something derogatory about the law of God.

'Of all the commandments, which is the most important?'

'This: that the Lord our God is the only Lord. You must love the Lord your God with all your heart, all your soul, all your mind and all your strength.' I was quoting from the early part of Deuteronomy, and now cited Leviticus: 'The second is this: "Love your neighbour as yourself." There is no commandment greater than these.'

He saw that I had gone to the heart of the matter,

showing that without love, obedience is both impossible and unacceptable.

'Well said, Master. You are right in saying that God is the only God, and to love him supremely and your neighbour as yourself is far more than offerings, sacrifices, ceremonies.'

'You are on the verge of the kingdom of God,' I said.

A large delegation of priests had been gathering, and I turned to them. 'What is your opinion about the Messiah? Whose son is he?'

'The son of David,' they replied.

'Then why was David inspired by the Holy Spirit to call him "Lord"? For in the Psalm he says, "The Lord said to my Lord: Sit at my right hand until I put your enemies under your feet." So if David calls him "Lord", how can he be his son?'

Not a man was willing to risk a reply, or ask for the explanation; by which they missed much. In fact, they retreated some distance, resolved never again to debate with me — the one whom David called 'Lord' because he was not only older than David but pre-existent to this world; the one who was David's son because he appeared in the earthly scene in David's lineage, as Son of Man.

Today would be my last day of teaching in the temple; what I was about to say would be my concluding address. How could I rouse the religious leaders to see themselves as God saw them? How could I break the chains that bound the masses to tradition and to the men who indoctrinated them with tradition?

Speaking to the ordinary people and my disciples, I said, 'The theologians and Pharisees are your teachers. By close observation you will find that their lives are inconsistent with their exalted profession of righteousness, and that they burden you with much that is contrary to the Scriptures, much that springs purely from human tradition.

'In spite of their outward piety, you will find that their

hearts are full of self. They love to be honoured; they love to be addressed by titles of reverence and veneration — titles by which you must address no human.'

I faced the spiritual leaders. 'You are exceedingly zealous, sparing no pains to win one convert; and when you have won him, you make him twice as fit for hell as you are yourselves. You are blind guides! You see holy things in a distorted way. You do not suspect it, but there is hypocrisy in you. Your prayers are long and sound fine, but you shut up the kingdom of heaven to men — nor do you yourselves get in. Your words sound holy, but when I send out men to teach my doctrines you will persecute them!'

I had my hand up, speaking as a judge. I saw how they would stone Stephen and kill James and many others, all under the influence of my adversary. My wrath came from the Holy Spirit, and was directed not at these important and influential little men, but against Satan and every agency he used to falsify God's truth.

I dropped my hand. This was a sad moment, a moment of farewell. Oh, that all these dear people, and these doctors of religion, would give themselves heart and soul to my Father!

With a lingering look at the temple, deep compassion for the people, and a sense of destruction to come upon all this and all these within their lifetime, I choked out, 'O Jerusalem, Jerusalem, you who kill the prophets and other divine messengers, how often have I longed to gather your children together as a hen gathers her brood under her wings! But you would not let me. Look, here is your temple, desolate, by God forsaken! You will not see me again until you say, "Blessed is he who comes in the name of the Lord!" '

Going to the Court of the Women, I paused opposite the contribution chests. Many rich people came up and deposited large sums. Then a poor widow shuffled up and dropped in two tiny copper coins.

This must go down in history. I called my disciples.

'Believe me, this poor widow has just given more than all the others. They gave out of their plenty, she out of her poverty. In fact, she put in everything she had to live on.'

As we moved on I was made aware of my disciples' thoughts. I had come off best in every verbal battle with the priests and theologians; but in a way this was a hollow victory, they felt, because our chance with these men was lost. If only I had performed a miracle to overawe my enemies, to strike them to their knees with my thunder! They ached with disappointment. Now there was a final break with the men of influence, and our prospects seemed hopeless.

I felt saddened and depressed at my disciples' state of mind.

Just then Andrew and Philip found us in one of the inner courts. 'Master, there are some Greeks outside who have come to worship in Jerusalem, and they would like to meet you!'

My spirits at once lifted. I had not closed my eyes in sleep for thirty-six hours, and today had been a hard day; now my Father, ever gentle and understanding, was sending me encouragement.

'The hour has come for the Son of Man to be glorified!' I said. The great ingathering of the Gentiles! These Greeks were an assurance of it, an advance deposit, a message from my Father . . . here where I stood in the shadow of the cross. 'Let us go to them!' I said, and was led to the court of the Gentiles.

They were a clean-faced little group, enquiring of eye, respectful, earnest. My heart went out to them.

We exchanged a few words of courtesy. I motioned for them to sit down, and found a perch for myself on the steps. There was a genuine heart hunger in these men . . . but a terrible trial awaited their faith.

They had heard of my triumphal entry into Jerusalem.

But the reports were exaggerated: I had driven the priests out, taken over the temple, and was about to be crowned as King.

And while exhilarated by these expectations, they were soon to see me dead on the cross! It was enough to shatter their faith.

'You men have come just in time to witness my glorification,' I said. 'Glorification, did I say? Let me tell you with great emphasis: a kernel of grain *must fall to the ground and die* — otherwise it remains only a single seed. Do you realize what I am telling you? Only when the seed dies does it produce a harvest!'

They blinked at me. I was talking about death, not a throne!

'And, friends, what about people who wish to be followers of mine? The person who loves his life will lose it, whereas the person who hates' — my way of underlining 'loves less' — 'his life in this world, will have it throughout eternity! And, friends, whoever wants to serve me must take me as his pattern: what I stand for, my servant will be. Whoever serves me will be honoured by my Father in heaven.'

My mind was carried away to the millenniums-spanning work of redemption, right through to my death that was now so near. My humanity shrank from the voices of mockery, the false charges, Peter's blatant disloyalty. The leprosy of mankind's guilt was about to touch me. Worst of all, my Father would have to turn away from me, treating me as lost mankind deserved.

I felt surrounded by a pall of gloom, and exclaimed, 'How great is my distress! For what shall I pray? Father . . . save me from this hour!'

I felt sick. My Father would have to abandon me, as he must eventually do with all who refuse to abandon their sins. It was unbearable, worse than physical pain and death. A tide of faintness threatened to overwhelm me.

I gathered strength from the Holy Spirit and prayed, 'No, Father! Do *not* save me from this hour! That's why I came! Father . . . *glorify your name!*'

The pall had lifted; a cloud-like presence hovered above me. From it came a voice: 'I have glorified it, and will glorify it again!'

It was the voice heard after my baptism in the Jordan, and again on the hill of transfiguration. The crowd cowered and said it was thunder; some said an angle had spoken to me. But only the Greeks had seen and understood: it was primarily for them. Now, and henceforth, they were sure who the Messiah was — despite the cross.

I said, 'This voice spoke for your sake, not mine. This is the hour of decision, which will be reflected in the judgement. The Prince of this world is about to be unmasked and suffer loss. But at the same time I will draw all to myself, when I am lifted up from the earth.' The words were cryptic, but after seeing me on the cross they would understand better.

Yet some at once grasped that 'lift up' involved death, and a man said, 'Our Law teaches us that there is no end to the Messiah. But you say the Son of Man must be lifted up — what does this mean? Who is this "Son of Man"?'

He was like a man endowed with the faculty of sight, yet groping blindly in daylight. 'The light is among you. But not for much longer. Now is the time for you to walk in this light, otherwise darkness will overwhelm and confuse you. While you have the light, put your confidence in it so that the light may shine in you as well!'

Glancing around, I cried out, 'When a man believes in me, he believes in him who sent me! My words are the Father's, my authority is the Father's. I came bringing light. Those who reject my words will meet them again in the judgement!'

I left the temple. The people had seen my multitudinous signs, yet few would believe: they were fulfilling Isaiah's prophecies about their voluntary blindness and deafness. At this stage a significant number of leaders believed in me, but feared to go on speaking in my favour lest they be banned from the synagogue. Men's opinion mattered more to them than God's.

THE SECOND COMING 65

With a large retinue of people I was leaving the temple when my disciples, anxious and puzzled because I had told the priests their temple was being left desolate, pointed to the massive walls. 'Master, look at the enormous slabs, the magnificent stonework!'

I shook my head and said sadly, 'Take a good look at all this. I assure you, not one stone will be left on another. Everything will be demolished.' There were gasps and hisses of astonishment among the people.

Soon able to shake off the crowd, I made my way down to the Kidron and up the Hill of Olives, taking along only Peter, Andrew, James and John. I was shading my eyes against the low western sun, staring down at the city and its temple, when one of the four asked with concern in his voice, 'Please tell us three things. When will these things happen, and what will be the sign of your coming, and of the end of the world?'

They still hoped, in spite of all I had said about my death, that I would proclaim myself King any day now. But, they reasoned, I told the temple crowd less than two hours ago that they would not see me again until they exclaimed, 'Blessed is he who comes in the name of the Lord.' Evidently I would go away, then return in power and glory to claim my kingdom. And I had talked about total destruction in Jerusalem — which surely meant the end of the world . . . .

They were confused, but I was not. I saw Jerusalem

destroyed in about forty years' time; then a long time when my faithful ones would be persecuted almost to extinction; then my return in heavenly glory and power. What could I say that would help them, not this week, but in the months and years ahead — and at the same time help the faithful ones of future generations understand time and events a little better?

How easy it would be to give them exact dates! This was simplicity itself for the Divine Spirit. But then the destruction of Jerusalem, a generation away, would no longer convey a sense of urgency; and the events beyond that would seem impossibly remote and no challenge to a daily life of faith.

At the other extreme, how simple just to say, 'Forget signs of the times; forget about trying to understand where you are in history. Just live each day as if it were your last. Then, no matter what happens, you'll be ready!'

To stimulate my followers in searching the Scriptures; to make them intelligent and not merely blind followers; and to make them partners in knowledge, children instead of servants . . . I would give them special insights, not merely an injunction to be ready.

And so for these four, and for all my future eager-minded followers, I set out some prophetic mileposts, providing only as clear a glimpse as my listeners could endure.

First: the destruction of Jerusalem and the temple, and the scattering of the nation that had rejected its Messiah.

Watch out for deception — false messiahs, who will be accepted by many. Do not be alarmed by wars and turmoil, famines and earthquakes, as tokens of the coming of a messianic deliverer. Instead of being the beginning of deliverance, those signs are the beginning of calamity.

Persecution will break over you. You will be hated by all nations for my sake, and killed. Among you many will turn traitor. So-called prophets will lead many astray. Your love will be tested.

Close to the time of Jerusalem's destruction will be this sign: armies about Jerusalem — an 'abomination of desolation' predicted by the prophet Daniel. Flee at once to the mountains. Pray that your flight will not expose you to the rigours of winter, and will not disrupt the peace of your Sabbath observance.

Second — there will follow a time of religious persecution unequalled in history. Were it not cut short, none regarded by God as true believers would survive it.

Third — my second coming. Once more false prophets, false messengers, false messages, false advents. When invited to go and see messiah-christs inside a city or away from it, do not go — they will be false. Yet they will work great signs and miracles, almost sweeping even the elect off their feet! Their miracles will be no reason to put your trust in them. They will all be false christs, I say, because the true Christ will come as the lightning flashing across the heavens from east to west. He comes in celestial clouds, with power and glory, sending out his angels with fanfare of trumpets to gather to his side his elect from all over the earth.

When will he come? The Father has not made known the day or hour. It will be in times of calamity and trouble; it will take people by surprise as much as did the flood in Noah's time, because it will be a time of absorption in worldly things. Blending in with Jerusalem's experience, love will grow cold as worldliness increases, fellowbelievers will betray one another, you will be hated and persecuted for my sake. And there is this great sign: this Gospel of the kingdom will be preached in all the world as a testimony to all nations — then the end will come. He who stands firm and loyal to the end will be saved.

While I was talking, Tuesday ended with the setting of the sun. As twilight deepened, lamps and torches were lit below us in the city, and we could make out a bridal procession by torchlight.

I said, 'When the day of my coming arrives, something like this will happen. Ten girls took their lamps and went out to meet the bridegroom. Five were foolish, five wise. The foolish ones took no spare oil for their lamps; the wise ones did. The bridegroom stayed away longer than expected and all ten dozed off to sleep.

'At midnight a cry roused them: "Here is the bridegroom! Come out to meet him!" The foolish said to the wise, "Our lamps are going out. Give us some of your oil!" "No," came the reply, "there will not be enough for us and you. Go and buy some for yourselves."

'While they were away the bridegroom came. Those who were ready went in to the wedding with him, and the door was shut. The other five came and pleaded to be allowed in, but he replied, "I do not know you." So you see, you must be ever on the lookout — you never know the day or hour.'

Aided by the Spirit, they would eventually see the deeper lessons: the foolish were not hypocrites, but still missed heaven, being destitute of the 'oil' of the Holy Spirit which only closer attention to the lamp of the Scriptures could have given them — something the midnight time of spiritual darkness on earth would particularly demand.

To illustrate the responsibilities involved in being followers of mine, I launched into another parable.

'A man going on a journey distributed his money to his servants — five talents to one, two to another, one to a third; each according to his capacity. The first put his five talents to work and gained another five. So did the two-talent man, but the one-talent man dug a hole and buried his talent.

'After a long time the master returned and settled

accounts with them. He praised the men who had multiplied their talents in serving him, assuring them of happiness. To the man who had done nothing with his single talent he said, "You lazy good-for-nothing, you will lose your talent to the man who has done most! Your place is outside, in misery and darkness!" '

In the final day of judgement the spiritual drifters, the dodgers of heaven-sent opportunities to witness for me, will be classed with evildoers . . . .

The greatest sin among people is this: man's inhumanity to man.

Because my Father is a God of love — gentle, kind, patient, merciful, forgiving, caring — inhumanity of any kind is obnoxious to him. And the strangest thing is that man will in God's name and my name persecute those of other interpretation and persuasion! That form of inhumanity called religious persecution is to God nothing short of loathsome; it proves a diabolical spirit, no matter how it might be dressed up with pious mouthings about the glory of God and his Christ. In fact, joining God's name to inhuman behaviour compounds the sin, adding to heartlessness the sin of blasphemy.

I saw the years of persecution stretching ahead, torture, burnings at the stake, burials alive, drownings, massacres, bakings alive near a fire, and other forms of Satanism — more often than not in my name! — and shuddered.

I was exhausted, not having slept in two taxing days and a night; but before gathering my robe about me and lying down on this hill between the rocks to sleep, I had a last message for my followers.

'John, James, Peter, Andrew — when the Son of Man comes in his glory, accompanied by all the unfallen angels, he will sit in majesty on his throne. As a shepherd separates the sheep from the goats, he will decide everyone's fate. The "sheep" will receive eternal life in the glorious kingdom of my Father; the "goats", along with the devil and his angels, receive the opposite.

'What standard will the Son of Man apply? Love . . . as shown in compassion, concern. He will say to the righteous, "You fed me, clothed me, cared for me, visited me in hospital and prison" — and they will be surprised to learn that the compassion they showed the poor, sick, persecuted and lonely, was regarded in heaven as kindness shown to the Son of Man!

'You see, the spirit of kindness flows from God, and is channelled through humans in whom God's spirit lives. God's love embraces the fallen, the erring, the sinful, the suffering; and every deed of kindness to uplift a fallen soul, every act of mercy, is accepted as done to the Son of Man.

'Just so, those who are self-absorbed or indifferent or cruel, will have a rude awakening when they discover that in heaven's view I was the one they passed by without a thought for my plight, I was the one they persecuted!

'I am heaven's sacrifice for man's redemption. Without this sacrifice none can ever be saved.

'But, do you see, some will be saved by my sacrifice without ever having heard of the Son of Man. Born in pagan cultures, they respond to every glimmer of light brought to their consciences by the Holy Spirit, and bless all about them with their divine spirit of kindness. They never had a chance to read the law I wrote on Sinai — but they prove that the divine law is written in their hearts. They prove that they are living and working side by side with the ministering angels. By virtue of my sacrifice, they will not perish.

'So I say to all my followers, seek out the stranger, the lonely, the persecuted, the discouraged, the sick, the starving. And in your kindness to them, show how much you love me.'

After sleeping on the hill that night, I spent most of Wednesday alone in prayer. The twelve disciples found me on the hill and listened with their usual mystified silence to my statement, 'You know that in two days' time it will be Passover, and the Son of Man is to be handed over for crucifixion.' I explained that I wanted to eat the Passover meal with them a day in advance of the official time.

'Where, Master?' Judas was quick to ask.

Knowing that he had been in touch with the religious leaders again last night, and had agreed to point out a place and a time where I could be arrested privately, I said, 'I will make that known tomorrow.'

After a time, when I was ready to wander off to be alone in prayer once more, he asked casually, 'Will you be spending the night at Bethany, Master?'

The home of Lazarus, Martha and Mary would make an ideal place at night for my arrest. 'No, not Bethany,' I replied; and I slept on the Hill of Olives again, alone, being careful to choose a different spot from the previous night.

On Thursday morning I spoke to my disciples about the spiritual kingdom. Afterwards, because this would be our first day of the Passover time, the day to prepare for the Feast, Peter and John asked, 'Where do you want us to make preparations for you to eat the Passover?'

None had a greater interest than Judas Iscariot in knowing the address in Jerusalem. But I did not want our meal to be disrupted with my arrest, so I said to the two men, 'As you enter the city you will find a man coming towards you, carrying a jar of water.' This would be unusual — a man doing 'women's work'.

'Follow him to the house which he enters,' I went on, 'and give this message to the owner of the house: "The Master wishes to know where the room is in which He may eat the Passover with his disciples." He will show you a large room upstairs, furnished and ready. Make the preparations there.'

They went, finding everything as described. After sunset, when Friday had come, they returned and we followed them into the city.

Our occasions together were usually times of tranquillity and joy. Tonight I was troubled. This showed on my face, provoking concern in their eyes.

They had entered this room with feelings of jealousy and resentment. As they straggled behind me on our way down Olivet, they were bickering over which of them should occupy the most important position in my kingdom. When we came into this room, Judas, set on having the highest place if there was one, tried to get the seat on my right. John had already taken it so Judas took the one on my left; and for a while various men glowered at one another.

With an aching heart I said, 'Oh, how passionately I longed to eat this Passover with you before I suffer! For I tell you, I will not eat it again until it reaches fulfilment in the kingdom of God.'

I fell silent and waited. For a moment they were touched by my sadness, then their ruffled feelings gained the upper hand in looks and whispers.

I looked at the pitcher, basin and towel, placed in readiness for a servant to perform the courtesy of washing our feet before the meal. There was no servant; one of my disciples should do it. But there was resentment against John for having appropriated the place at my right, resentment against pushful Peter, against ambitious James, against the one who glowered here or muttered there. None would kneel, none would serve another.

At last I rose. They fell silent, watching. Laying aside the loose cloak which had been my blanket the past two nights, I wrapped the towel round my waist as a slave would do, poured water into a basin — and knelt before Judas Iscariot.

To be first was his obsession, so I would serve him first. It was not difficult to kneel and serve Judas: had I not in heaven laid aside my majestic crown and royal power to take on lowly humanity in order to serve man?

I would not expose his dark secret to the others. Hungering for his soul, I took his dusty feet in my hands, washed them and wiped them while silently pouring out my heart in prayer. As the love of heaven spoke to him, his hands started shaking. He was close to tears, ready to throw himself before me in confession. How gladly would I have put my arms about him and forgiven him! Judas trembled on the verge of eternal life . . . and pushed it from him.

'What would this detestable sycophant John think of me if I confessed I was a traitor? And the others? And how can a king debase himself by serving others like a slave? Surely there's no chance that he is Israel's King!'

He had previously told himself that his treachery would never lead to my arrest. I would summon miraculous power, assert my Kingship, and after my crowning thank him for having forced my hand. Now he was sure there would be no kingdom; he had been deceived in me.

I turned away, unutterably sad, and served the others. They sat frozen in shame and humiliation.

Peter: 'You, Lord, kneeling before me and washing *my* feet?'

'You cannot understand now what I am doing. You will, later.'

'Never will I allow you to wash my feet, Lord!'

'If I do not wash you, you have no fellowship with me.'

'In that case, Lord, not just my feet. Wash my hands and head as well!'

But he and the other ten had not lapsed into complete apostasy; I was symbolically helping them purge themselves of certain character defects.

'He who has had a bath needs no washing but for his feet. The rest of him is clean. And you are clean — though

237

not every last one of you.' Judas heard, and knew that I knew.

John's turn came last.

Now there was union of heart. Humility and love had washed all except Judas.

'Do you understand what I have done for you? You call me Master and Lord, and rightly so — that is what I am. As I, your Lord and Master, have washed your feet, you must also wash one another's feet. I have set you an example. You must do as I have done for you. I tell you emphatically, a servant is not greater than his master, nor a messenger than the one who sent him. Knowing this, blessed are you if you do it.'

THE SUPPER

To a considerable extent, the past three-and-a-half years were a will-making time for me. That 'last will and testament' would within hours be sealed by my death. Any important change or new doctrine would be introduced before that ratifying death.

For thousands of years sacrificial offerings, ceremonies and annual feasts had pointed to my death. These would fall away today, being fulfilled. In their place I was instituting, as memorial of my sacrifice, the service of this supper.

Before me were the paschal lamb, bitter herbs, lettuce, other vegetables, a sauce made of almonds, dates, figs, raisins, spice and vinegar; as well as unleavened bread and the fruit of the vine. Only the last two would be elements of my service. Yeastless and free of fermentation, they were suitable to represent the sinless life, the uncorrupted sacrifice of the Son of Man.

Taking bread I blessed it, broke it and gave it to the disciples with the words, 'Take and eat. This is my body, which is for you. Do this as a memorial of me.'

In their wonderful new mood since my service of humility, they took the fragments, solemn, earnest, in the grip of a mysterious joy and peace. This was how I wished it.

Then: 'This cup is the new covenant sealed by my blood, which is shed for many for the remission of sins. Drink of it, all of you.'

They did so, and I added, 'I tell you, I will never again drink of the fruit of the vine until that day when I drink it with you under totally new circumstances, in the kingdom of my Father.'

The Passover commemorated the divine deliverance of Israel from Egyptian slavery. My ordinance of the Lord's Supper would commemorate the infinitely greater deliverance from sin and the second death. At the same time it points to my second coming, man's blessed hope.

By partaking with my disciples of the two elements of the Lord's Supper, I pledged myself as their Redeemer.

'When we have finished here, we go to Gethsemane,' I said for Judas Iscariot's ears.

I had just served him with the bread and the cup. Even now my disciples did not suspect him.

'When I said you are all clean, I was not speaking about all of you. I know those whom I have chosen. But the divine foreknowledge enshrined in a text of the Scriptures must be brought to light: "He who eats bread with me has turned against me." I mention this now, before the event, so that when it happens you may have your faith confirmed that I am what I am. And by accepting me, you accept the One who sent me.'

The thought of what Judas was doing to himself overwhelmed me. I struggled with my emotions, and said, 'The fact must be faced — one of you is going to betray me!'

Shocked stares. Incredulity; then, remembering that I had never said anything that proved less than perfectly true, fear and self-distrust.

'Lord, am I the one?' John exclaimed.

I shook my head, and a chorus of similar cries went up. John, prodded by Peter, whispered a question and while others were calling for my attention I murmured in his ear, 'It's the one whose hand will be in the dish at the same time as mine; I'll hand him this morsel of bread.' A moment later this was done, and John knew.

'The Son of Man will pass away, as the Scriptures predict,' I said. 'But woe to the man who betrays him! It would be better for him if he had never been born.' It was a soft-spoken invitation for Judas to utter the words that would save his life; but his face was rigid, sealed off from us.

'Am I the one, Lord?' It was James. Others were just as insistent. I made no response.

Silence gradually settled. Eyes were turning to Judas: he was the only one who had not put the question. Becoming aware of the implications of his silence, Judas turned to me.

'Am I the one, Lord?' he asked stiffly.

'The words are yours.'

My words were gentle, ambiguous to the others but not to him. It was his last chance. My eyes appealed to him. The slightest response would save him, and the priests would come searching for me on their own, finding me with greater difficulty; but he would live. How I pleaded with him in that look!

He got up and turned away. To shield him from an outburst on the part of the others if they realized what his sudden departure meant, I said, 'Do quickly what you will be doing,' and they thought because he handled the money I had given him a task, something to buy or donate.

My adversary now had full possession of him. He went out into the night.

In leaving, Judas had passed the point of no return. My betrayal and death were at hand.

I said, 'Now is the Son of Man to be glorified. At the same time, God is to be glorified by the Son.'

The eleven needed a further word to prepare them for my separation from them. 'My children, I am to be with you only a little longer. I repeat what I told the Jews: where I am going, you cannot follow.'

There were flickers of fear. They pressed closer to me.

'I am giving you a new command.' In Leviticus I gave them the command to love others as they loved themselves. My new command would intensify that injunction. 'You must love one another *as I have loved you!* Then everybody will identify you with me.'

Peter was too agitated to concentrate on the love commandment. 'Lord, where are you going?'

'You can't follow me . . . yet you will, later.'

'Lord, why not now? I'll lay down my life for you!'

That's what I meant, Peter. 'Will you? In point of fact, before the rooster crows you will have disowned me three times.'

'Lord . . . !'

My gesture silenced him: the less he said, the fewer words he would have to swallow before this Friday was over.

'Children, I said I was going away. But don't be devastated by your feelings. Trust God, and trust me. In my Father's vast dwelling place there is ample room. I'll be preparing a place for you. Then I will return and take you there . . . . You know where I am going, and how to get there.'

'But, Lord,' Thomas protested, 'we don't know where you're going, so how can we know the way there?'

'I am the way, the truth, the life!'

That I am the way was true for Adam, Noah, Abraham,

Moses — men who never heard of Jesus of Nazareth, yet knew that there was no eternal life unless God provided the sacrifice that released them from the death penalty. It is true for all who see their salvation in God's works and not their own.

Every word, every act of my life, is to be your standard of truth.

'No one comes to the Father except through me. By knowing me you know the Father. From now on you do know him — you have seen him.'

'Lord, show us the Father, and we ask nothing more!' exclaimed Philip.

Amazed at his dullness, I said, 'Have I been with you so long, Philip, and you still do not know me?' What spirit and character do you think I have been displaying all along?

'Anyone who has had me before him has seen the Father! Then how can you say, "Show us the Father"? Don't you believe that I am in the Father and the Father in me? That my very words are inspired by him? Believe me, all of you, when I affirm my unity with the Father; or else accept the evidence of the things I've done!'

They were awed. Peter, James and John especially, because they had been on the Hill of Transfiguration.

'And when it comes to my deeds, those who have faith in me will do them. Because I go to the Father, they will be enabled to do even greater things.'

I was thinking of how my life was, humanly speaking, ending in rejection and failure; how I was restricted in space by accepting humanity; how I would send the Holy Spirit to represent me in ubiquitous power, to convert thousands in a day through the testimony of my widely scattered followers.

'And I will do whatever you ask in my name, so that the Father may be glorified through the Son.' Strength and grace would be theirs as, forgetful of self, they strove to glorify the Father through the Son.

The Holy Spirit would teach them that to pray 'in my

name' was not a magic formula, nor a mechanistic procedure. Even evil spirits acknowledge me as 'Jesus' and 'the Holy One of God', as did the spirit whom I cast out in the Capernaum synagogue; and many people calling me Lord and doing miracles in my name will hear me say I never knew them. No, praying in my name is more than using a name: it also means accepting my character, manifesting my spirit, and doing my works. Such proofs are beyond demons, but natural to my Spirit-led followers.

'If you love me, you will obey my commandments,' I went on, making the test of a true disciple graphic. 'Then I will ask the Father and he will give you another Helper to be with you for ever — the Spirit of truth. Lacking spiritual perception, worldly people cannot receive him. But you know him, because he lives with you — indeed *in* you. Through him, if you obey my teachings, my Father and I will make our home with you.

'Whoever knows my commandments and obeys them, loves me. He who loves me will be loved by my Father and me, and I will reveal myself to him' — in sustaining power and encouragement, especially under persecution.

'When I am no longer with you, the Helper, the Holy Spirit, will help you to understand all things and will revive my teachings in your minds. So never fear: you have my peace with you.

'Remember my words. I am going away, to the Father, and will return some day.

'The prince of this world is approaching. By no test or temptation will he be found to have got the better of me. In everything the world will see my love for the Father, as shown in my obedience.'

I led them in singing the joyful words: 'O praise the Lord, for his merciful kindness is great towards us. The truth of the Lord endures for ever!'

'Now, let us go forward to face what is coming,' I said.

We moved through the dark crowded streets, and as we left the city gate and started down the valley I said, deeply sad, 'Tonight you will all leave me in the lurch.'

Peter at once responded with vehemence, 'Others might leave you in the lurch, Lord, but not me!'

'Simon, Simon, it has been Satan's express purpose to sift you all as wheat. But I have prayed for you, Simon, that your faith may not fail. When you are converted, encourage your fellow believers.'

'But, Lord, I am ready to go with you to prison and to death!'

'I am telling you, Peter, before the cock crows twice, you will have disowned me three times,' I repeated.

Even more emphatically he said, 'If my life is at stake, I'll never disown you, Lord!'

Much the same sentiments came from the rest, and I said, 'The Scriptures predicted, "I will kill the shepherd, and his flock will scatter". But remember this. When I have risen, I will meet you in Galilee. In Galilee.'

I carried their minds back more than a year to their mission tour. 'When I sent you out without purse, bag or extra sandals, were you ever short of anything?'

'Never, Lord.'

In the bright moonlight I saw a grapevine and said, 'I am the true vine and my Father is the gardener. You are the branches. Every unfruitful branch is cut off by him. To bear fruit, a branch must have a living connection with the vine. If the life forces flow through, the branch will bear much fruit.'

As 'life forces' I emphasized three things: love for God; obedience to my commandments, which are also my Father's commandments; and love for one another.

'Of course, if you are really spiritually fruitful the world is going to hate you, because you will be different from those about you. But remember, the world hated me first. My servants must expect to be treated as I was treated. Be forewarned: they will even banish you from their congregations. In fact, a time will come when those who kill you with think they are obeying God! That will betray their fundamental ignorance of God. Remember, just such people witnessed my miraculous life — and rejected me!'

We were down in the valley now, and I reminded them that they would have heaven's richest gift — the Holy Spirit. 'When he comes, he will convict the world in matters of sin, righteousness, and judgement. Being of one mind with the Father and me, he will guide you in all matters of truth.'

I could see that they were worried.

'You are wondering why I have been harping so much on my going away, then returning. I came from the Father, and I am going back to him. While the world rejoices in events about to happen, you will weep and mourn. When that happens, draw on my Father for strength and comfort. Then . . . I will come back, and your joy will know no bounds.'

Impressed because I had read their minds, they said, 'This reinforces our belief that you came from God!'

'At last you believe! But remember, you are going to be scattered. You are going to leave me in the lurch. But my Father will be with me. When your troubles come, take heart! I have overcome the world.'

The time had come for my parting prayer with them. Lifting my eyes skyward, I prayed, 'Father, now that the hour has come, glorify your Son, that the Son may glorify you. Through him you offered eternal life — which is found in a true knowledge of you and Jesus Christ whom you sent. Glorify me with the glory we shared before this planet existed!

'I have revealed you to those you gave me out of the world. My Father, protect them by your power! Protect them from the evil one! Sanctify them by the truth: your word is truth!

'And bless the others who will in future believe. Grant them the same unity that you and I have, so that their faith in us may be authenticated to the world. Father, I long for the day when these people will be with me in my kingdom of glory!'

IN GETHSEMANE

The city of pilgrims' tents glimmered in the light of the full Passover moon, and the silence had a faraway echoing quality. I looked at the garden of olives opposite and felt dread building inside me. Not dread of the armed men and priests soon to appear, but of something incomparably greater.

I loved Gethsemane and often went there for prayer. Now it was like a monstrous black creature that preyed on all who strayed into its web.

I set one foot ahead of the other, moving towards the web, feeling desolate. Since the first dawning of my human consciousness I had walked in the light of my heavenly Father's presence. This was my life. Not for one moment had my conscious contact with the Father been broken. To do always those things that please him was more precious to me than the breath in my lungs, the throb of my heart. To be shut out from my Father was agony and horror unmitigated. And that was happening to me now.

The eleven were dismayed. Never had they seen me in the grip of such sadness. They were alarmed to see me stumbling. I took another step, swayed, and they jumped to support me.

At the gate I left eight to pray for themselves and me, taking Peter, James and John deeper into the garden. Looking into their faces I knew that even this was not enough privacy. They had seen me transfigured on the hill; I could not bear to have them witness my suffering at close quarters.

'Wait here, in prayer with me.'

A little distance from them, but within sight and hearing, I went down prostrate and felt black waves beating at me. The prophet Zechariah's words came to me: 'Awake, sword, against my shepherd, against the man who is my companion, says the Lord of hosts.' The three heard my cry, 'Oh, my Father, let this cup pass me by!' and they prayed anxiously, but after less than an hour were fast asleep.

All the sins of mankind, past, present and future, must now be placed on me. My soul recoiled from the touch of guilt. I had never broken one commandment of my Father's moral law, never gone against the slightest prompting from his Spirit. My adversary had surrounded me with the most subtle and fiercest temptations. I had felt his power, but had never yielded. To taste sin, to feel the embrace of slimy self-ishness and rebellion, was more than I could bear. It would sweep me from the Father's presence. I groaned and shuddered.

I heard the sad, sympathetic voice pleading, 'If you accept man's guilt your separation from God will be eternal! Don't do it, friend! And what would you gain if you made such a sacrifice of yourself? Man's ingratitude! The Jews, claiming to know God better than anyone else, have rejected you. They have sworn to kill you! A disciple who has walked by your side for two years has betrayed you. And look at those three, asleep. All will desert you. Sin can't exist in God's presence. Accept it, and the life will be crushed out of you for ever. Never, never, never will you see your Father's face again . . . .'

It was my adversary. But so much of what he said was true. I knew he was desperate. He had been preparing for this last battle for three years. It was now or never. If he could get me to back out, the plan of salvation would collapse; God would have proved unwilling to pay the supreme price to save his own creatures; the accuser's charges against God's loving character would seem proved; his own position would be reprieved. If he failed, he and his angels and his principles were doomed.

But . . . so much of what he said was true.

I prayed, groaned, shuddered in the grip of my special temptation, my most terrible temptation — to exert my divine power and leave all this behind.

As I wiped my brow I saw the blood on my hand.

I needed sympathy, a little warmth from a human being, and lurched to where the three lay. They woke up, but hardly knew me and seemed to shrink from my face.

'Simon Peter, have you been sleeping? Couldn't you stay awake in prayer with me for an hour?' John moaned, wide-eyed, as though in the grip of a nightmare. 'You men should be awake in prayer. Temptation lies ahead.'

They seemed in a stupor, eyes becoming heavy, breathing deepening. Sympathy for them overwhelmed me and I said, 'The spirit is willing, but the body is weak.'

Feeling faint, exhausted, I found I was staggering as I returned to my place of prayer, to wrestle again with the temptation to let the human race bear the consequences of its own rebellion.

The second time my presence roused them from their sleep. The sight of my face filled them with fear. They had no word of comfort or sympathy for me, and I went back to my retreat.

It was not too late to wave away man's cup of guilt. My disciples heard the words that wrenched from me and wanted to offer help — but I had told them to stay where they were. This was the moment of truth. If I turned away the entire human race would perish. If I accepted, my Father must turn away from me. This was too much for my human nature. Yet . . . how can I abandon you, believers in God?

'If this cup must not pass me by, if I must drink it . . . oh, Father, your will be done!'

Past exhaustion, past fainting, I fell to the ground in the throes of death. The angel who stands in my Father's presence came to revive me and support me while I drank that cup of guilt.

Later. I was steady on my feet, calm. Wiping the blood from my face, I went to my disciples. They had been drifting into and out of sleep.

'Still sleeping?' I asked softly. 'Resting mind and body?' I heard the armed men coming. 'Up now! Let us go. The one who has betrayed me is coming.'

Gathering all eleven, I was waiting near the gate where moonlight splashed between two trees when the soldiers, temple police and priests arrived with Judas Iscariot at their head.

'Who is it you want?' I asked.

'Jesus of Nazareth!'

'I am he.'

The angel who had revived me moved between us and the mob with their torches, cudgels, swords. They recoiled and collapsed, priests and soldiers. Before all the witnesses, visible and invisible, this was my chance to escape. I stood, waited.

Like men coming to life they sat up dazed, gathered their wits and struggled erect, uncertain, holding back.

Softly I asked once more, 'Who is it you want?'

'Jesus of Nazareth.'

'As I told you, that is who I am. If I am your man, let these disciples go.'

The police had insisted on verification of my identity. Judas, who had also collapsed at the glimpse of glory, gave the prearranged signal by stepping up and kissing me fervently on the cheek with a 'Greetings, Master!'

I accepted his kiss, and gently asked, 'Friend, why are you here? Judas . . . are you betraying the Son of Man with a kiss?' Folding his arms, he stood stiff-backed and tall, but I saw the trembling of his hands.

Emboldened because Judas had touched me with impunity, they laid hold of me and tied my hands securely with a rope.

'Lord, shall we strike them with these swords?' some of the eleven cried, and Peter drew a sword and lunged at Malchus, servant of the high priest, missing his head but severing his right ear.

'Enough of this!' I said to the police, freeing my hands with a movement, taking the ear and restoring it so that the Sanhedrin would have no charge of violence against us, and to give them the mercy of one more evidence of my Father's power working through me.

'Peter, put that sword away! All who take up the sword shall perish by the sword. Do you think I cannot now pray to my Father and receive twelve legions of angels? But if I did that, what about the fulfilment of Scripture prophecy? No — shall I not drink the cup my Father has given me?'

I held out my hands for the rope and turned to the priests and other religious leaders.

'You have come at me with cudgels and swords, as against a criminal. Day by day I sat teaching in the temple. You had every opportunity of laying hands on me, but did nothing. The darkness of night is better suited to your work, isn't it?' They would never escape the force of those words.

The eleven were at the same time amazed and indignant that I allowed myself to be bound once more. With his heart in his throat, Peter mumbled, 'We'd better get out of here!' and they all deserted me and fled.

Jerusalem was asleep, but from somewhere a rowdy mob had materialized and followed us with jeers and shouts as I was dragged and bullied to the palace of Annas, former high priest.

The religious leaders of the nation had been trying for two years to build a case against me, with no success. Annas's questions showed that he was interested in getting me branded a blasphemer. That would shock the considerable number of priests and leaders who were secretly for me, and turn the common people from me.

Secondly, I must be found plotting against the Romans, who alone could allow a death sentence. To this point I said, 'I spoke openly to the world, in street, synagogue, temple. I did no secret work.'

On the matter of whether I had ever said anything blasphemous, what about their spies who had been after me for two years? 'Why do you ask me?' I said. 'Ask those who followed me about. They heard everything!'

This set Annas back on his heels. An official, seeing him discomfited, slapped me in the face. 'Is this the way to speak to the high priest?'

'Turning the other cheek', as I had taught my disciples, in the true figurative sense of staying calm and refusing to take offence, I said, 'If what I have said is wrong, please tell me where it is wrong. But if there was nothing wrong in what I said, why did you hit me?'

Finding he was getting nowhere, Annas took me under armed torchlit guard to his son-in-law Caiaphas, ruling high priest. Here, while waiting for the Sanhedrin to assemble, the two fruitlessly questioned me — an extension of the Annas inquisition.

Now I was before the great council in the judgement hall, part of the temple complex. Only about sixty members had been called, those suspected of being sympathetic to me having been left to sleep on. Caiaphas was on his throne, the judges on either side, and the Roman soldiers on the platform below the throne. I stood at the foot of the throne and noticed that besides myself no one was calm and serene.

'Well now, how about working a miracle for me?' Caiaphas sneered, and found me deaf to the words and to his subsequent questions.

How easy, I thought while he and others demanded replies from me, to break up this hearing, even without recourse to divine power. I could turn the Pharisees against the Sadducees by saying, 'One party here is set on killing me, for fear that I will call Lazarus of Bethany in my defence — and thereby prove the Pharisees right when they say resurrection from the dead is a fact!'

Or I could say, 'Why don't you charge me with Sabbath breaking?' That would soon bog down proceedings on the point that I had only broken their traditions, never the commandment itself; and would focus attention on my miracles of healing, which was the last thing they wanted.

They produced false witnesses and bribed witnesses, but there had been no time to rehearse the performance. Under the obligatory cross-questioning by the judges the men contradicted one another and sometimes even themselves.

Caiaphas was getting desperate. He knew there were ample witnesses to prove that I had called the priests and theologians hypocrites and murderers. But the Romans would shrug at such a charge; and in any case, those were the very words that his Sadducee party had hurled at the Pharisees. He could charge me with violating Jewish traditions; but the interpretation of traditions was another matter on which the Pharisees and Sadducees were at swords' points.

Then a matter was raised, the only one on which they could unite against me.

Three years ago I said, referring to my body, 'Destroy this temple, and in three days I will raise it up.' Two witnesses now said, 'This fellow said, "I can destroy the temple of God and rebuild it in three days." '

The high priest let his face show great shock. Leaning forward, he led the cross-questioning of the two.

My words had not only been taken out of context, but distorted. But I decided to say nothing to men blinded by prejudice. In any case, in spite of all the indignation now building up over these words, a man claiming he can do what they were saying is — if he is a mere man, as they said I was — to be pitied as insane, not killed in anger.

Caiaphas obviously felt he was getting nothing that would set the Romans against me. My silence maddened him, and my utter composure. Jumping out of his throne, his face contorted, the hands trembling that yearned for my throat, he shouted, 'Do you say nothing? What about this testimony against you?'

I had no desire to speak; and so went into fulfilment Isaiah's prophecy, 'He was oppressed and afflicted, yet opened not his mouth; he is brought as a lamb to the slaughter, and as a sheep is dumb before its shearers he opens not his mouth.'

He raved a while, then stopped. Raising his hand to heaven, he addressed me in the form of a solemn oath: 'I adjure you by the living God, to tell us whether you are the Messiah, the Son of God!'

He was admitting that the Messiah is the Son of God — something most of his spiritual successors would deny.

I felt I must accept the oath of this court. My Father's name was involved, and my Messiahship. I had told my disciples, 'Whoever confesses me before men, him will I also confess before my Father in heaven.' My example must reinforce my words.

'I am,' I said solemnly, knowing that I was making certain my death. 'But I say to all of you, in time to come you will see the Son of Man seated at the right hand of God, and coming on the clouds of heaven!'

For a moment he quailed before my gaze, seeing visions of the judgement he denied, of the hidden misdeeds of his life brought to light. Then in fury he let my adversary have his way with him, and tore his robes. 'Blasphemy! What need of further witnesses? You all heard the blasphemy! How do you vote?'

'Guilty . . . guilty . . . guilty. He must die!'

During this night trial by the Sanhedrin — illegal according to Jewish law, which required that capital charges by heard only by daylight — I noticed something, just after three o'clock in the morning, that deepened my anguish. John and Peter were in the courtyard behind me, having turned back from their headlong flight of three hours ago. John stood in a corner, as near to me as he could get. Without drawing undue attention to himself he was making no secret of the fact that he was a disciple of mine.

But Peter worried me. He was in the back of the court, trying to blend in with the crowd, warming himself at their fire, laughing at their jokes. Inwardly he boiled with anger at my accusers, and with more than impatience at me because I was letting it happen.

A girl who worked for Caiaphas studied the conflicting emotions on his face and asked, 'Aren't you also one of this man's disciples?'

Shocked and confused, he blurted, 'I don't know what you mean. I know nothing about it!'

'No, wait!' She stopped him as he began to sidle away. 'Aren't you one of his disciples?'

Sweat broke out on his face. 'Woman, I don't know him!' he snapped, and a burst of laughter round the fire so nearly drowned out the half-hearted crowing of a rooster outside that it only registered at the back of his mind.

He shuffled his way to the porch, where the girl saw him again and pointed him out to others. Again he denied that he had ever had any dealings with me.

Nearly an hour passed. A bystander heard Peter making

a light-hearted remark and said, 'You must be one of them. I can tell by your Galilean accent!'

Peter lost his head. Desperate to prove that he had no dealings with the man of pure speech, he broke into curses and swore, 'I don't know this man!' At once the cock crowed, this time loudly because it was close to dawn.

He stood frozen, in a state of shock. I had to save him from despair. Turning, I put all the love I could into the look I gave him.

He saw. A sob burst from him. He swung on his heel and ran off blindly, colliding with people, slipping on the dew-wet flagstones, storming down streets, out by the gate, down the valley . . . and found himself in Gethsemane, to collapse in tears on the spot where I had sweated blood.

From time to time I had glanced in another direction also. Judas stood near a pillar, anxiously expecting that at any moment I would work a miracle to save myself and take over the throne from Caiaphas. As hour after hour went by before Annas, Caiaphas and now the Sanhedrin, and I submitted to all the abuse heaped on me, a terrible fear came to him that he had sold me to my death.

'Guilty, guilty, guilty!' the judges finally intoned. 'He must die!'

Something in Judas snapped. Soon after Peter had fled, his voice rang hoarsely through the hall and courtyard, 'He is innocent, *innocent!* Spare him, Caiaphas!'

The tall man was pushing people out of his way, pale and haggard, his forehead beaded with sweat. Rushing to the throne of judgement, he threw down at Caiaphas's feet the silver coins exchanged for my life and grasped him by his robes.

'Let him go! He's done nothing to deserve death! And take back your money!'

The high priest angrily shook him off, confused, speechless.

'I have sinned!' Judas wailed. 'I betrayed innocent blood!'

'What's that to us? That's your business!' Caiaphas exploded, his face mottled with fury at this public exposure of their conspiracy.

Judas stared up at me in helpless horror. Jumping to his feet, he screamed, 'It's too late! *It's too late!*' as he rushed out of the temple court into the darkness.

I was led through the courtyard to the guardroom to await the trial-by-daylight needed to preserve a show of legality. The rabble had seen how I was manhandled before the council, how I was illegally bound before being pronounced guilty, and treated with jeering and mockery. Now was their chance.

They used their hands, their fists and their spittle. Blindfolded me and shouted, 'Who's this hitting you now, Messiah?' Made fun of my body, thrust me to the floor, dragged me about. I made no sound, but John saw from the doorway and nearly died.

In Gethsemane my adversary had urged me to back out and leave men to perish. When that failed he changed his tactics. Now I was to be broken in body and spirit, worn down until, goaded beyond endurance, one word of anger or retaliation escaped me. Just one word — and God's sacrifice for man's guilt would be imperfect, the plan of salvation would collapse. And so these men and women exhausted themselves in assaulting me.

The sun rose nearly one and a half hours later; and when I was freed of my bonds and half carried in, it was like another man who stood before Caiaphas, someone dug out from under a rockfall.

This time the proceedings were perfunctory. He claims to be the Messiah. We twice heard it from his own lips. He is a blasphemer. Guilty. Death!

A satanic fury took possession of the people. With an

animal roar they rushed to get at me. Only the Roman soldiers' use of force saved me for the cross.

The commander turned on Caiaphas. 'Where do you get the authority to pronounce the death sentence? And let me remind you that it is even against your own Jewish law to condemn a man to death on his own testimony!'

Priests and rulers seemed maddened, hurling abuse at me. An old garment was thrown over my head, I was struck in the face and told to prophesy. When the garment was removed one poor wretch did not hesitate to spit in my calm face, swollen and bleeding. My accuser was still trying to wring one wrong word from me.

I hoped suffering men and women would remember who the source of suffering really is — my adversary. And instead of joining the accuser by blaming God for their pain, would remember how God suffered with his Son.

PILATE 73

Governor Pilate, seated on his judgement throne, was waiting. Ruffled at being called out of bed, he wanted this over with.

His gaze rested on me with severity. After long moments his expression softened. He was accustomed to signs of guilt, fear, boldness, defiance. 'Badly bruised face — mauled by those savages,' he thought. 'Yet . . . nothing but calmness and dignity.'

His hand went reflectively to his jaw. This was the man about whom he had been hearing from his wife. Cured thousands of sick people, even raised the dead . . . could *that* be true?

Abruptly rising, he looked me over searchingly. The Romans who had pressed in, driven by curiosity, gave way as he strode to the entrance. My guards responded to his nod and placed me behind him.

The crowd out there had been noisy and restless; now it cheered and roared. In the front ranks were the guiding lights of Israel: Sanhedrin judges, priests, teachers of the Law. They and their rabble wanted to eat the Passover meal this evening, and would be 'defiled' and disqualified if they entered the judgement hall. They stayed outside — oblivious of the fact that their murderous hatred had already defiled them. Strange how even the religious will do anything but allow the religion of God *into their hearts*.

Pilate demanded silence. 'Who is this man? Why is he here? On what charge?'

Caiaphas: 'Excellency, he is a deceiver called Jesus of Nazareth . . . '

'The charge, the charge!'

Caiaphas was snappish. A hearing was not necessary. 'If he weren't a criminal we'd not have brought him to you!' A murmur of approval from the leading men of the nation around him. Much less imposing delegations in the past had swept the weak and vacillating Pilate into unjust action.

Pilate half turned to me. He had heard about Lazarus. A man dead four days, raised to life? If they could bluster, so could he.

'If you're such august judges, why bring the prisoner to me? Take him back and judge him according to your law!'

Hesitation. 'Well, we have. We have passed sentence.'

'What sentence?'

'Death. But we need your signature. Excellency, take our word for his guilt. Sign it through. We'll accept responsibility.'

'I won't pass it unless you bring a charge against him.'

Whispered consultations; shouts and grumblings from the mob. Three days ago the religious leaders tried to trap me by asking, 'Is it right to pay taxes to Caesar, or not?' With my 'Give to Caesar what is Caesar's' they could do nothing. Or could they?

Caiaphas: 'We have witnesses here who will testify that

the criminal in there told people not to pay tax to Caesar! Where are those men? There you are. You heard that fellow stirring up the people with talk about not paying taxes, didn't you?'

Their voices, confirming this.

Caiaphas: 'He has tried to undermine our Roman government. He forbade the paying of tax to Caesar. And, charge number three: He sets himself up as Messiah, a King.' They knew better, especially on charges one and two. They were the nation's most respected and influential leaders in religion and society; but they were not above perjury.

Pilate snorted in disbelief. Turning, he asked, 'Are you the King of the Jews?'

Feeling the light of eternal truth on me, I said, 'It is as you say.'

'You heard his admission, Governor!' chorused the priests, and with the mob howled for my death. It was deafening.

Pilate was confused. 'Are you saying nothing?' he shouted at me. 'You heard their charges!'

'Yes! He made himself King! He wants our taxes! He's against Caesar!'

A roar of voices, waves of noise breaking over us. I felt detached from it all.

Astonished and fascinated, Pilate led me away from the tumult.

'Are you really the King of the Jews?' he asked, faintly anxious.

The Holy Spirit was working with him. Unless he responded, my death today would be in vain as far as he was concerned. I sent up an earnest silent prayer for him.

'Are you asking because you are personally interested, or merely because of what others are saying?'

I saw the conviction, before his gaze wavered and he exploded, 'Do you take me for a Jew? Look here, your own nation and religious leaders brought you before me. What *have* you done?'

He had missed the opportunity of his life. Was it worthwhile saying anything further? Perhaps . . . just to go the second mile.

'My kingdom does not belong to this world. If it did, my men would be fighting to get me out of the hands of the Jews. No, my kingship has nothing to do with this world.'

'Then you are a King?'

' "King" is not my choice of word, but yours. My sole mission in life is to champion the cause of truth. All truth-seekers pay attention to what I have to say.'

His eyes lit up and he exclaimed, 'What is truth?' Then he seemed startled at the fervency in his own voice, and swung away to cover his embarrassment. What a tragedy, not to wait for the answer!

Stalking to the entrance, he shouted, 'I find no guilt in him!'

Rage erupted like a volcano. Gradually words could be made out: 'You're unfaithful to your governorship! You're siding with an enemy of Caesar! We'll report you in Rome!'

More cultured accents: 'The whole nation knows of his seditious work! He has all of Judea stirred up! It started in Galilee and has spread as far as this city.'

Pilate was disgusted, but also afraid. 'Galilee?' he said, and came back to me. 'Herod Antipas rules Galilee. I hear the king is here for Passover . . . ' He gave orders for me to be taken to Herod, murderer of John the Baptist.

NOTHING MERITING DEATH 74

Herod was all smiles. He listened for a few moments to the barrage of priestly accusations, then raised a hand.

'Silence! So you are Jesus of Nazareth! These people have obviously been ill-treating you. Soldiers, untie him!

You priests, how can you treat a man like that? It's inhuman! Uncivilized!

'Now, prisoner, they say you are a blasphemer. Is that true?'

The Holy Spirit had pleaded with the corrupt king for years, even after he had John beheaded; but I saw that the Spirit had left him. All the pearls brought to him had been trampled under swine's feet. Because of his disdainful treatment of heavenly light, any light offered him now only hardened him even more. I would not assist the process.

'Look, prisoner, I am sorry for the way these devils treated you. I can help you. Tell me, are you really a prophet?' In reply he received heaven's supreme rebuke — silence.

He had cripples called in from the street and ordered me to heal them. Silence. I'm anxious to see if your fame is well founded! Silence. You've worked miracles for others: work one for your own interests now! Silence. I'll make you a promise. Heal one of these cripples, and I'll know you're a prophet and set you free! . . . How the religious leaders froze at these words — they feared nothing so much as an exhibition of power. Their desperate voices: 'He's a blasphemer, O King! He works his miracles through Beelzebub the prince of devils!'

Consternation everywhere. Herod, who trembled in his sandals when he first heard of me, fearing that I was John come to life, said pompously, 'You don't seem to know whom you're dealing with. I am the king who had John the Baptist's head removed from his shoulders! My word is life or death! Here, this man with the shrivelled leg — cure him!'

A few words from me, exposing his secret life and the horror of his approaching doom, could have set him shaking from head to toe. I neither looked at him nor spoke.

'He's nothing but an impostor!' he screamed in rage. 'Listen, you! If you won't speak to me, if you won't obey me, I'll ratify the Sanhedrin's death sentence! I'll hand you over to your enemies! They'll teach you how to talk!'

This was all the encouragement the crowd needed. Descending on me like wild animals, they plucked me this way and that, pounded me on the head, dragged me about by the feet. Herod joined in the sport.

When my own blood blinded me, the Roman soldiers intervened for the second time that Friday to force back a maddened throng intent on tearing me limb from limb.

Now Herod and his soldiers mocked me, stripped me, slung one of Herod's old cast-off robes over me to parody my kingship, heaped abuse on the one whose patience would not waver.

But something else was also happening. Some who stepped forward to bow mockingly looked into my eyes and abruptly turned away, silenced. Herod was reaching for my face when he hesitated, the jeering laugh dying on his lips. Most remained boisterous, crude, cruel; but some fell silent.

'Your Majesty, you said you would ratify the sentence if this charlatan failed to . . . ' It was High Priest Caiaphas, very eager.

'I've changed my mind. I — I'm sending him back to Pilate.' Fear had taken over.

Governor Pilate was very unhappy to have me back.

'What do you expect me to do?' he fumed. 'I *have* examined him! I found no guilt in him. You've proved nothing against him. I sent him to one of your own faith, King Herod, and he found nothing in him that required the death sentence. So . . . '

The mob hissed and snarled. The indignation of the sixty-odd members of the Great Sanhedrin blazed at him. Determined to let me go, he desperately wanted a softening in the crowd. Surely, I must have friends among them! Wasn't it reported that I had cured thousands? He would work on their sympathies for a suffering man.

'I'll let him off with a flogging!' he decided.

Flog . . . a man you have declared to be without guilt?

There was so much noise in the crowd that it was difficult to tell their verdict on Pilate's announcement. The priests were now briskly moving about in the mob. They could see how the rabble intimidated Pilate into unjust acts. The feelings of the mob must be swept up to the highest pitch.

A note had been handed to Pilate, and while the soldiers waited for instructions on my flogging he opened it. His hands shook as he read it and his jaw slackened.

I was shown what had happened. As a result of my prayer for him nearly two hours ago, an angel from God gave Pilate's wife a dream. She saw everything — my trial before Herod, the trials before Pilate, the torture, the envy and malice of the priests, my crucifixion, my return to earth in divine glory. She woke up in the grip of a terror such as she had never known.

He read her words, 'Have nothing to do with that righteous man! I have just been through torment in a long dream about him'; and he stared at me in fear.

'Wait!' he told the soldiers. He was remembering the practice of releasing a convict of the people's choice at Passover. It was a custom of pagan origins, which had always irked him because it lacked even a shadow of justice. Now it might help him in his quandary. He knew of an insurrectionist and criminal awaiting execution, a man so brutal and vile that no right-minded person could want him out of prison.

At the entrance he shouted, 'I'll free a prisoner for you! You all know Barabbas. Whom do you want freed, Barabbas or Jesus called Messiah?'

The priests had done their work well, and led the thunderous cry, 'Barabbas! Give us Barabbas!'

Pilate staggered visibly. This was impossible! He must have been misunderstood.

'No, I mean, the one I must *free!* You want me to free

the King of the Jews for you?' The title was out of his mouth before he knew it.

'Away with this man! Free Barabbas for us!'

He was speechless for a moment, then desperately stammered, 'Wh-what then shall I d-do with — with Jesus called Messiah?'

The crowd roared demoniacally, 'Crucify him! Let him be crucified!'

It was not too late for Pilate to do what he should have done earlier: issue a command to disperse the crowd. Within five minutes there would be no rabble, no dignitaries, no intimidatory noise. Then he could let me go. I would still be killed today, because the priests would take the law into their own hands; but Pilate would be free of my blood. The warning to his wife was evidence of heaven's love.

But he dithered. 'Why, what wrong has he done?' he asked almost plaintively, and for answer received a savage roar.

'Tell me — what wrong *has* he done? I find nothing in him to merit death! I'll — I'll have him flogged, and let him go.'

Their frenzy knew no bounds. 'Crucify him! Crucify him!'

The soldiers stripped me to the waist, turned my back to the crowd, and applied the three-thonged, metal-loaded scourge. I was faint with fatigue and covered with wounds before they started. As the lashes tore open my back the crowd howled with delight . . . an explosion of sound that came thirty-nine times.

I must bear the torture; must not retaliate; think no impatient thought; indulge no self-pity; shun anger; not let the divine nature help the human nature bear this; not let the angels deliver me. The plan of salvation had to be perfected.

They had demanded a miracle as evidence of my kinship with God. In my response to the cruelty and the agony they had, could they but see it, conclusive evidence.

'Now crucify him!' the people screamed.

Pilate, close to the end of his tether, sent for Barabbas. While he waited, the soldiers led me aside, flung an old purple cloak over my shoulders, wove a crown of thorns and pushed it down on my head, put a cane in my hand and made fun of me.

Barabbas and I were presented to the crowd side-by-side in the courtyard. In a pleading voice Pilate, pointing at me, said, 'Behold the man!'

The robe slipped from my shoulders. The pain, exhaustion and loss of blood had taken their toll; but I stood unbowed, Son of God, telling them in my expression of heaven's gentleness and tender pity for my enemies . . . and I saw some in the crowd weeping.

'I've brought him out to let you know I find no case against him!'

The priests started to chant: 'Crucify him! Crucify him!'

In a lull Pilate cried despairingly, 'Then you take him and crucify him! I find no guilt in him!'

The priests shouted, 'We have a law, and according to that law he must die, because he claimed to be the Son of God!'

Pilate, taut with a new fear, took me into the judgement hall. 'Where do you come from?' he asked, more than half convinced that I was a divine being.

I said nothing. Heaven had no further light for him.

'Don't you answer me? Don't you realize I have power to crucify or release you?'

In harmony with my Father, I wanted to excuse this unworthy ruler as far as possible.

'You would have no authority at all over me, if heaven had not granted it to you. But I will say this: the greater guilt lies with the man out there who handed me over to you' — High Priest Caiaphas, representative of the nation and its religious institutions.

In terror of his conscience, and in greater terror of the multitude, Pilate tried to set me free; and the Jews cried, 'If you let him go, you are not Caesar's friend! He claims to be a King. That makes him Caesar's enemy!'

He pleaded with them; they threatened him with a report to the emperor. Time passed. He grew more confused, thought more and more of his own position, own security, in the face of a riot.

From his portable judgement chair: 'Behold your King!'

'Away with him! Crucify him!'

'Shall I crucify your King?'

Caiaphas, the judges of the Sanhedrin, then the crowd: 'We have no King but Caesar!'

Water in a basin; he washed his hands.

'I am innocent of the blood of this righteous person! See to that yourselves.'

Caiaphas, then the rest: 'Let his blood be on us, and on our descendants!'

Barabbas set free; I, led away for the flogging preceding crucifixion.

HE SAVED ONLY OTHERS   75

On at least eight occasions over a period of nine months I told the twelve disciples that I was going to die. Two weeks ago I said, 'We are going up to Jerusalem, and the Son of Man will be betrayed to the religious leaders. They will condemn him to death and hand him over to the Gentiles. They will mock him, spit on him, flog him and kill him. Three days later he will return to life.'

Two days ago I said, 'You know that in two days' time it will be Passover, and the Son of Man is to be handed over for crucifixion.' And just ten hours ago I said, 'Tonight you will all leave me in the lurch.'

With all these forewarnings one would expect them to

be ready — anxious but self-controlled. But they all panicked and fled. Of the two who turned back, one — Peter — disowned me with a show of extreme weakness and fled a second time. And the other one, John, was so bewildered that he failed me — and himself — in a moment of dire need.

I was led out of the Praetorium after the second flogging, and found the cross prepared for Barabbas awaiting me at the gate of Pilate's court. It was placed on my lacerated back and I exerted myself to carry it, but my body was too far gone. I found that I was lying in the street, pinned down by the weight of the cross.

The soldiers tried once more, lifting me to my feet, placing the cross where I was so willing to have it; and again I collapsed . . . determined to the death not to use the power of my divine nature, determined not to resort to the Holy Spirit for the power with which I had helped others to health or life.

There was a vast crowd, choking the street and house tops in all directions. At my first collapse they burst into jeering laughter, shouts of derision. When my legs gave way the second time the mockery was deafening; and as it subsided I heard a mournful wailing.

Rising unsteadily I looked at the weeping women. They were not believers in me — this was human sympathy, a vestige of dignity in humanity. After all the malice and cruelty of the past nine hours — an eternity of nine hours — it was like a drink from a cool spring.

Then sympathy for them overwhelmed me. I saw their city besieged by the Roman legions in a few years' time . . . .

'Daughters of Jerusalem,' I said, 'don't weep for me! Weep for yourselves, and for your descendants! The time is coming when you will bless childless women, when people will pray for mountains to fall on them. If men treat the green tree, fruitful and innocent, like this, how will the dry tree, barren of righteousness, be treated?'

And now I needed help — someone to carry my cross. Many of you in the crowd were shouting five days ago, 'Hosanna to the Son of David! Blessed is he who comes in the name of the Lord!' Will you volunteer? Or where are you now, self-confident Peter? John, I see you there, looking as if my torture had been inflicted on you. Will you come forward and say, 'He is my Lord! I will carry his cross!' Or will you also leave me in the lurch? Will you honour me, and honour yourself in the annals of the kingdom? Or will you fail me . . . .

He looked stricken; he wiped his tears; but even John never moved to lift my cross.

They found a man. No Jew would carry the defiling thing. He was a foreigner — Simon, of Cyrene in Libya. Having heard of me from his believing sons Alexander and Rufus, he pushed his way through the crowd and was standing there saying, 'Oh, no! No! No! This is terrible! Poor, poor man!' when rough hands gripped him.

'So you're sorry for him, are you? Then carry his cross for him!'

For the rest of his life he was to be grateful for this privilege.

There was my poor mother, supported now by John, blinking at me through her tears, remembering the visit to the temple when I was 12, remembering the miracle with the water at Cana, and expecting me still to display my power and deliver myself from my enemies. And, between hope and despair, yearning to cradle my head in her arms, to wash the blood off my face.

Behind them, Mary of Bethany, crying herself blind, led by Salome and James's mother Mary.

The road seemed never-ending. Shouts reverberated off houses, off the portals of a city gate. Minutes later, in more open ground, screams, a wave of horror sweeping the crowd.

A lifeless tree. Poor Judas Iscariot, in a remorse without

repentance, had climbed up, fixed a rope on the branch and round his neck, and jumped. The dead branch broke, he plunged into a projecting splintered branch which disembowelled him under his own weight . . . and stray dogs had been feeding on him.

The crowd shivered in a sudden chill. They were witnessing judgement.

The priests came alive, clustered round the scene to block the view, feverishly ordered the mangled corpse dragged away and buried without ceremony . . . .

Three crosses — and three of us. The two struggle loud and long, are subdued. I stretch out my arms, hold still for the spikes; my mother faints and is carried away. Sweat pours down my face.

'Father, forgive them! They have no idea what they are doing!' The Roman soldiers do not know, nor do much of the crowd blindly following leaders who should have known better; nor many in coming ages who would 'crucify' me with their sins . . . . Willing ignorance, deliberate ignorance, does not remove guilt; but I would invoke no vengeance on my enemies. In the spirit of my Father I must pray for them.

The nails have gone through flesh and bone. The cross is lifted by strong men, violently thrust into the hole; flesh and sinew give way.

Soon after nine o'clock Pilate's inscription arrives to be placed above my head: 'Jesus of Nazareth, the King of the Jews', in Hebrew-Aramaic, Greek and Latin. This is the fate of any King of the Jews, Pilate is saying. The Jewish leaders who shouted, 'We have no King but Caesar!' protest that this is unacceptable, now seeing that in their hatred of me they sacrificed their national interests; but Pilate is unmoved.

The thousands of pilgrims from various countries will read the inscription and be drawn to investigate the Scriptures — a mind higher than Pilate's had chosen the words.

As predicted by the twenty-second Psalm, the soldiers divide my sandals, girdle and other pieces of clothing among the four of them, and cast lots for my tunic.

A strange gloom, like a dark cloud, surrounds the hilltop.

Spiced wine is offered me: its stupefying effect would deaden the pain. Tasting, I realize what it is and refuse it. My mind must be unclouded, to keep faith strong.

The priests, led by my adversary and his angels, lead the mob in mocking me. 'If you're the Son of God, come down from the cross!' Yes, that would be easy; but how can your sins be removed unless the Holy One from God takes your death sentence on himself? You're asking me to abandon the human race to death!

'He saved others. But now he can't save himself! Let Messiah the King of Israel come down from the cross, and we'll believe!'

You acknowledge before all history that I saved others — from disease, death and the grave. That is why you should believe.

'He trusted in God. Let God deliver him then! He claimed to be the Son of God!'

Yes, I trusted in God all my life, as you admit — that was my character and my life.

Both robbers being crucified with me at first made mocking, bitter remarks, but one has become silent and thoughtful. He is thinking of Pilate's 'I find no guilt in him', of the inscription, my bearing, the things he has heard and is hearing.

His companion jeers at me, 'If you're the Messiah, save yourself and us!'

He: 'Don't you fear God? You are under the same sentence! And we deserve what we're getting. This man is innocent!' He turns his head to me, yielding fully to the Holy Spirit. 'Jesus, remember me when you come into your kingdom!'

At this moment, when every appearance is against us, I assure him of salvation. *Today,* when we hang as condemned criminals on the cross, I assure him of life eternal. *Now,* when I am ridiculed for apparent inability to save myself, I assure him of access to 'the tree of life, which is in the paradise of God', where the crystal water of life will 'flow from the throne of God'.

'You will be with me in paradise!'

His faith grasps the assurance. His whole face is transformed by joy in the beam of light which penetrates the gloom. I am 'counted with the transgressors', as Isaiah foretold, but cannot be robbed of my power to forgive sins.

My mother could not stay away. Here she is, leaning on John's arm. I must make provision for her.

'O woman,' I say respectfully, 'he will be a son to you.' And to John, 'There is your mother!'

At noon an intense darkness settles over the entire crowd and the Golgotha hill. The raucous shouts die away. Men tremble, and many try to grope their way to the city. From time to time there is whimpering and wailing.

My physical pain is hardly felt, so great is the other agony. Others have familiarized themselves with evil, acclimatized themselves to it from birth. I have not. Its malignancy torments me, as does the fact that man is blinded to its enormity. Since Gethsemane I have been bearing all the evil generated by mankind — and its keenest edge of anguish is loss of the sense of my Father's presence.

By mid-afternoon the darkness shifts from the crowd to their city and the Judean plains; but not from me. I cry, 'My God, my God, why have you forsaken me?'

I know why. In God's judgement the second death — which I am tasting — is the lot of all who are found with the sins which I am now bearing.

Some of the darkness lifts from me. The physical torment reaches a peak and I mumble, 'I am thirsty.'

A Roman soldier is moved with pity, dips a sponge on a

twig of hyssop into something vinegary and offers it to me; but my own people offer me only renewed mockery.

Suddenly the cross is bathed in light and I cry, 'It is finished! Father, into your hands I commit my spirit!'

SEALED AND SECURED 76

John the apostle:

When my Master cried, 'It is finished', the inner curtain of the temple, between the holy place and the most holy, tore apart from top to bottom. The place was no longer sacred. The Great Sacrifice had taken the place of all sacrifices and offerings for sin.

We all stood paralysed, gazing at the Master as darkness again rolled in with a rumbling of thunder. An earthquake shook the earth, and we found ourselves in heaps on the ground. 'Surely, he *was* the Son of God!' the centurion in charge of the soldiers screamed.

In the dense darkness of the past three hours the Father was — unrevealed — with his Son at the cross: suffering with him, reconciling the world to himself.

In the murder of the Master the great rebel angel overreached himself. First he tried to discourage Jesus into backing out of the plan for saving man. When this failed he tried by mental and physical torture to provoke him into one error — anger, retaliation, the abandonment of faith in his Father, an act of self-preservation. Again he failed. Jesus persisted sinless; he held on to faith and submission to God.

The whole universe witnessed the contrast between the rebel's lies, hatred, and violence, and Christ's innocence, patience and self-sacrificing love. Satan had unmasked himself and forfeited his influence in the universe. It was seen that with Satan are compulsion, intolerance, suffering and death; that with God are freedom, love, mercy and life.

It was seen that the controversy is not merely between

good and evil on earth, but it is a cosmic war between God and the mighty usurper created being.

God's weapons are the elements of his own character: love, patience, freedom of choice for all created beings — even rebels — humility and self-sacrifice . . . and he wins on the glorious note of Christ's cry, 'It is finished!'

From now on the issue is clear: faith and obedience to God, or obedience to the rebel. In the fullness of time the defeated rebel, his angels, and his human followers will meet their end; but all who love God will live on — active, growing intellectually and spiritually, living fulfilled lives, happy. 'It is finished' — God has triumphed.

The earthquake subsided. People began to collect their wits and move about, unnaturally quiet. Because sunset would usher in God's Sabbath, the Jewish leaders wanted the men off the three crosses. Pilate ordered the men's legs broken so that they would not be able to escape during the night or the next day; after the leg-breaking they could be taken down.

The soldiers, using two spears, broke both legs of the first man while he screamed in pain and cursed them. They hesitated at the middle cross, as if afraid to touch it, then applied their spears to the other man's legs, breaking them with cracking sounds while he moaned a shuddering prayer. The two were taken down and dragged aside to die their slow death from loss of blood or infected wounds.

At this moment the wealthy leader Joseph of Arimathea, up to now a secret believer in Jesus, arrived with a messenger from Pilate. The body of Jesus was to be handed to him for burial.

The centurion, not a man easily ruffled, went uncertainly to the cross. 'Is he really dead?' he asked, as if talking to himself. 'I've never seen a man die on the cross. Not even the same day. I've seen them last three days, four days. But he . . . '

He tested him for a heartbeat, and shook his head. 'Shall we break his legs, sir?' asked the men uneasily.

'Thrust a spear into his heart!' a knot of priests urged, anxious to make sure that the one they feared was dead.

A soldier thrust his spear deep into Jesus's side, piercing lungs and heart. He plucked it out, and with my own eyes I saw two copious and distinct streams, one of blood, the other of water. My record of this is true. In these things I see a fulfilment of Moses' words to the effect that the Passover lamb's bones were not to be broken, and of Zechariah's, 'They will look on the one whom they pierced.'

Of what did my Lord die? A broken heart. His heart was broken by mental anguish. He was killed by my sins, the world's sin.

Rabbi Nicodemus, no longer secretive about his faith in the Master, arrived with a large quantity of expensive myrrh and aloes for the embalming.

Gently and reverently the two men removed the body of my Lord from the cross, and I saw their tears falling on him. They wrapped him in strips of linen with the spices, and we laid him in Joseph's new tomb cut in rock in the garden next to Golgotha. The heavy stone slab was rolled against the entrance, and when we left to go and open the Sabbath, Mary Magdalene and the other Marys lingered tearfully behind.

Many of the Friday crowd could get no rest on that Sabbath. There was only one topic of conversation. During the sacred hours they searched their souls in the presence of certain prophecies of Scripture; and they never again took part in the annual paschal rites, having found their Messiah. Many priests were convicted of the true character of the Son of Man.

The leaders remembered what Judas had told them: Jesus said he would rise the third day. They knew a reaction against them was setting in, and felt even less secure than when the Lord was alive.

On the Sabbath they hurried to Pilate. Standing outside his door they said, 'Sir, the impostor claimed that he would rise on the third day. Give an order for the tomb to be made tamper-proof for three days. Otherwise his disciples may steal his body and say it came alive, which would only make matters worse.'

Pilate detested them and showed it. 'Take a guard and seal the tomb to your satisfaction!' he barked.

Sabbath or no Sabbath, those priests and Sanhedrin leaders supervised the work. They were in the grip of a cold terror. Ropes were lashed across the rock slab and secured to spikes driven into the rock. Everything was sealed with the Roman seal. One hundred soldiers under a centurion were stationed around the tomb, with orders to let no one come near.

How God must have smiled, I always think as I read the second Psalm.

HE IS RISEN! 77

The Sabbath ended with the setting of the sun, and my Lord was still in the tomb. All through the dark hours of Sunday the Roman soldiers kept their vigil, as did the host of fallen angels, all intent on keeping that tomb sealed forever.

Just before daybreak an earthquake like Friday's shook the earth, and there were flashes of lightning and a roar of thunder. Gabriel and another of God's angels appeared in a blaze of light, and the hosts of darkness fled. The soldiers, clinging to the earth for dear life, saw Gabriel touch the slab of sealed rock and roll it away as though it were a pebble.

'Son of God, come out! Your Father is calling you!' he cried.

My dear Lord came out, majestic and glorious. As Gabriel, the other angel, and an angelic host a little farther back bowed before him in adoration, he proclaimed, 'I am the resurrection and the life!'

Overwhelmed, the soldiers dropped off in a dead faint.

When they came to, they gaped for a while in the light of their torches at the empty tomb, then stumbled off towards the city. Almost at once they met people shaken out of their beds by the earthquake, and blurted out everything to them. These ran off to tell the priests, who were restlessly pacing about because of the same earthquake.

Alarm and consternation resulted. Caiaphas barked orders. Priests descended on the approaching soldiers and diverted them to a hall where the Sanhedrin men were assembling.

'Tell us what happened,' said Caiaphas.

'We were chatting. In the light of our torches everything was normal. Then an earthquake, and light blazing from above like the sun. A being full of light came down, effortlessly rolled away the rock, called to the corpse inside, "Son of God, come out! Your Father is calling you!" And . . . and there he was, crying, "I am the resurrection and the life!"'

Ashen-faced, Caiaphas tried to speak, but his voice was gone. All the priests stood petrified.

'We must go and report to the governor,' the centurion said.

'No! Wait!' The high priest was fighting blind panic. 'Men, you will have to help us! You must say his disciples came and stole his body away. While you slept — yes, while you were asleep!'

'Asleep?' The centurion was incredulous. 'My hundred men asleep on guard duty? We'd put ourselves under sentence of death!'

Caiaphas and his men had a persuasive argument — money. It was fetched, a huge amount, and displayed before the popping eyes of the soldiers.

'N-no!' quavered the centurion. 'Our lives are worth all the money in the world!'

'Your lives won't be at stake,' Caiaphas said flatly, looking round at his fellow priests and receiving nods. 'We'll put in a word for you. And let's face it, Governor Pilate won't want a report circulating that the man he called King of the Jews has come to life and is roaming about the countryside. Why, it would be an open invitation to everyone to flock to this man and rise up against the power of Rome! Don't you see that? It's in the interests of Rome to cover this up! If you refuse you're not only being disloyal to the interests of your Roman administration, but denying yourselves this money as well!'

They all went to a very unsleepy, nervous Pilate and told the story. He took his guard aside and questioned them. They broke down and told him the truth. He was terrified. This was ominous in the extreme. He could not let it get back to Rome that he had condemned an innocent man to death after declaring him innocent. The less said the better. In that he needed the help of these soldiers, these priests . . . .

While it was still dark that morning, Mary Magdalene started on her way to the tomb. She arrived after the soldiers had left with the greatest news of time and eternity, found the stone rolled away, and hurried off to tell the disciples.

Other women who had stood by the cross on Friday, including Mary the mother of James, Salome and Joanna, were approaching the tomb and worrying about getting the rock rolled away so that they could anoint the Lord's body with the spices which they had bought after the sun set on Sabbath. Suddenly the earth trembled, and there was a blaze of glory in the sky that had nothing to do with the rising sun. They hurried to the tomb. There was a soft light shining all about it. Gabriel, now not in overwhelming heavenly glory but reassuringly as a young man, although his face and clothes shone with Hill of Transfiguration light, sat on the slab of rock which he had rolled away.

As they turned to run, he said, 'Do not be afraid! I know whom you are looking for — Jesus the Nazarene, who was crucified. He is not here. He has risen, just as he said he would. Come, have a look at the place where he lay!'

Inside they saw another angel sitting on the stone slab where Jesus had lain, who said to them, 'Why are you looking for the living among the dead? He is not here. He has risen. Think, and you will remember how he told you while still with you in Galilee that the Son of Man was to be delivered into the power of sinful men and crucified, and how he would come to life on the third day.'

'Now,' said Gabriel to them, 'go quietly and say this to his disciples and Peter: "He has risen from the dead and is going ahead of you to Galilee. You will see him there."' How merciful that 'and Peter': to encourage the one who felt shattered because he had disowned his Lord! And how much it would help to restore him in the confidence of his brothers.

Their hearts palpitating with awe and joy, the women raced off with the news.

Meanwhile dear Mary had found Peter and me and was sobbing, 'They've taken the Lord out of the tomb, and there's no sign of where they've put him!'

I outran Peter to the tomb, and while waiting for him at the entrance saw the strips of linen inside. He rushed past me into the tomb, and I followed him. We saw the lengths of linen, and the burial cloth that had been around our Lord's head, all neatly folded and placed in separate piles. A rush of memories thrilled me as I recalled how Jesus foretold his resurrection.

Mary arrived and stayed when Peter and I left. Then an amazing thing happened to her. Tearful with grief, she peered in and saw the two angels seated on the burial slab.

'Woman, why are you crying?' they asked.

'They have taken my Lord away,' she sobbed, 'and I don't know where they've put him.'

She half turned and in her overwrought state vaguely saw a man, whom she took to be the gardener.

'Woman,' he asked softly, 'why are you crying? For whom are you looking?'

With her sobbing she heard his voice indistinctly — oh, how often we hear his voice indistinctly when grief or self-pity have overwhelmed us! — and choked out, 'Sir, if you've carried him away — tell me where you've put him and I'll — take him off your hands.' She was thinking of Lazarus's empty tomb, where she could put her Master's body.

Then she heard the dearly loved voice: 'Mary!'

'My Teacher!'

She leaped forward as if to embrace his feet, but he stepped back, hand raised. 'Do not hold on to me now, because I must ascend to my Father. Instead, go to my brothers and say to them, "I am ascending to my Father and your Father, to my God and your God." '

The group of women found the eleven disciples and other followers of the Master, and told them of the two angels at the tomb and the message that Jesus had risen and would meet them in Galilee. But the men did not believe the women, because they seemed incoherent; and in any case it seemed likelier that the body of Jesus had been spirited away by his enemies.

Then Mary Magdalene arrived and breathlessly poured out her story of speaking to the Lord. For the second time there was a message about meeting in Galilee.

Somewhat later the women who saw the two angels were walking near the city, still looking for disciples to whom they could tell the news, when the Lord suddenly met them with the greeting: 'Shalom!'

They clasped his feet and worshipped him, something he had not allowed Mary earlier because he did not want to delay ascension to his Father. Then Jesus said to them, 'Do not be afraid. Go and tell my brothers they should go to Galilee. They will see me there.'

So we received the message a third time. How merciful, how patient! And how dull and blind we were. We still felt uncertain and perplexed. Were the woman hallucinating along lines of wishful thinking?

And new trouble was crowding upon us. We had just heard that the story was going the rounds that we had broken open the heavily guarded tomb and stolen the Lord's body! This could only mean a fresh plot against us, fresh danger. How we longed for the presence, comforting and wisely helpful, of our dead Lord!

RISEN INDEED! 78

Most of the day there was a look of desolation about Peter. The bottom had fallen out of his world. Not only had our Lord allowed himself to be killed by our enemies but, almost more shattering, he himself had disowned his Lord. The cowardice, callousness and profanity of it overwhelmed him.

In the afternoon he left the upper room and wandered disconsolately to the Hill of Olives. In despair he stretched himself between the rocks and held his head in his hands, groaning whenever he remembered the cursing and swearing of his denial, and the lingering look the Lord had given him. He had no hope, no courage to face the future.

Then Jesus appeared to him, spoke to him, gave him that same look of love . . . and disappeared.

On the other side of Jerusalem two disciples, obscure quiet men who had hardly ever been noticed, were dragging their feet dejectedly towards the village of Emmaus. They were totally disheartened.

'Could this man, who allowed himself to be so utterly humiliated — could he ever have been the Messiah?' one asked. And they had loved him so much, with all their devotion! The path blurred before them and they wiped their tears and snuffled.

They became aware that a stranger had joined them. 'You look sad,' he said. 'What have you been talking about that depressed you so much?'

Ashamed of their tears, they kept their faces averted. One, a man named Cleopas, said, 'You must be the only person out of touch with what has been happening in Jerusalem!'

'What has been happening?' the stranger asked.

'All this about Jesus of Nazareth. He was a prophet, a man of power in word and deed before God and men. Our chief priests and other religious leaders handed him over to be killed, crucified. And we were so full of hope that he might be the Messiah who would liberate Israel!'

'And where is he now?'

'Well, this is the third day since it happened. This morning some of our womenfolk turned up with the startling story that they went to the tomb and failed to find His body. Instead, they saw a vision of angels who said he was alive. Some of our people rushed to the tomb and did find it empty, but they saw nothing else.'

The stranger said, 'What lack of understanding, and what sluggishness to believe all that the prophets said! Wasn't it clear that the Messiah had to suffer these things, and then enter his glory?'

Beginning at Genesis, he went through all the Scriptures, picking out those Messianic prophecies which Jesus of Nazareth had so perfectly fulfilled all the way to Golgotha. Then he showed them the prophecies of the promised one's resurrection, quoting also the things Jesus himself had foretold; and explained that the Messiah's coming in glory as King of kings was yet future.

'And why is it that the disciples of Jesus of Nazareth are so slow to see and grasp these prophecies of Scripture? Their sluggishness means that the death of Jesus destroyed their hopes — whereas that same crucifixion was convincing proof to Joseph of Arimathea and Nicodemus that Jesus was the true Messiah!'

They listened enraptured, glowing with new faith and hope. The sun set, marking the end of a very eventful Sunday. At Emmaus, in heavy dusk, the stranger began to take leave of them.

'No!' they exclaimed. 'We can't let you go! You must stay the night with us!'

They soon had a simple meal of bread and fruit ready. The stranger reached out and blessed the food, and the gesture was reminiscent of only one person. They started back in astonishment. Then, for the first time, they saw the scars in those hands where the nails went through.

'It is the Lord Jesus!' they shrilled. 'He has come to life!'

They jumped up to worship at his feet, but he vanished at once.

Overwhelmed, all they could repeatedly say was, 'Didn't our hearts burn in us, as he talked and opened the Scriptures to us along the way?'

It is interesting to me that had they not insisted on having the stranger as their guest, he would have gone on his way and they would never have known who it was that led them in a study of the Scriptures. He considered it more important for their faith to be established on the Scriptural evidence than on sight, and so their eyes were kept from recognizing him.

Leaving their food they started off in a fever of joy and excitement for Jerusalem, and in going over rocky patches in the dark could easily have twisted an ankle or suffered some other mishap had the Lord not, unseen, gone with them all the way to protect them.

The great Son of God, through whom all things were created and without whom nothing came into existence, was spending a good deal of time with two very humble men.

Arriving at the upper room in Jerusalem where we had cloistered ourselves for fear of the Jewish religious authorities, the men from Emmaus knocked. Inside, we stared wide-eyed at one another. Was this the moment? Soldiers from Pilate? Assassins from Caiaphas? Another knock, urgent, insistent. We were frozen in silence. Jesus died on Friday; would we meet the same fate today, Monday? Flogging, mocking, crucifixion? Could even one of us endure it as he had — patient, submissive, forgiving?

'Brothers! Are you in there? This is Cleopas!'

We could breathe again. My brother James unbarred the door. The two men entered — and another, entirely unseen, entered with them. Peter helped to bar the door against the enemy.

'We've come to tell you something so amazing you won't believe it!' Cleopas burst out.

'Wait!' said James. 'Here is the greatest news of all. Peter has seen the Lord!'

'He *has?* — But — but that's what we've come to tell you. *We've* seen the Lord!'

Panting, interrupting each other, stumbling over their words, they blurted out the story, and we stood clustered about them, spellbound.

'Unbelievable! It's too good to be true!' some exclaimed.

Then, the best-known, best-loved voice: 'Greetings!'

I whirled about. The Lord! The *Lord!*

Some of my friends staggered back in terror, thinking this a ghost.

'Why are you looking thunderstruck?' he asked gently, a slight smile on his lips. 'Look at my hands and feet. It is I — none other! Touch me — a spirit doesn't have flesh and bones, as you see I have.'

He showed us the nail marks in his hands and feet.

Seeing that most of us were too overwhelmed to credit the evidence of our eyes, he asked, 'Is there anything here to eat?'

Someone produced a piece of broiled fish, and he ate it to prove his humanness — so patient with our slack minds and slacker faith!

Oh, the joy that erupted in that room! Everyone was touching him, holding on to him, weeping and laughing at the same time. I felt I could not afford so much as to blink as I feasted my eyes on every line of that familiar dear face.

'I told you more than once that I was going to be killed, didn't I? I even said it would be by crucifixion. But I also said I would rise on the third day.'

As he had done with our Emmaus friends, he explored the Messianic elements of the Scriptures with us, showing how the Christ was to suffer sacrificially, atoningly, and redemptively on behalf of all mankind. Then he said, 'And all this, with all the truths you have seen in my life and heard from my lips, you are to preach to all nations — starting at Jerusalem!'

We were amazed. An immense, impossible work was being given us. The whole world to be reached! The whole world must respond with a yes or a no! It was staggering.

Then the Master impressed us with the secret of power — the Holy Spirit. In a symbolic act he breathed on us and said, 'Receive the Holy Spirit!' The more abundant impartation of the Spirit was only to come after the Lord's ascension.

When the Lord first met us in the upper room Thomas was not present. When we told him what he had missed he reacted in a strange way. I expected him, overjoyed, to praise God. Instead, he measured us with a hard stare and announced, 'I'm not saying you didn't see what you say you saw. But unless I see the nail marks in his hands and run my finger over them, and put my hand into his side, I can't accept this!'

It was so unexpected it took my breath away. How could any man be so difficult? Especially someone who loved the Lord as ardently as he did?

Then I remembered. When the women rushed in with their story of seeing the angels, I smiled indulgently and shook my head. Then Mary's meeting with the 'gardener' found me equally disbelieving. Not to mention listening with half an ear to Jesus's prior warnings, while holding on to the concept of a political paradise instead of a spiritual kingdom.

Deeply ashamed, I saw Thomas in a new light. He was probably wounded in his vanity because Jesus had revealed himself to the others and not to him. Jealousy had overwhelmed his good sense. That was how small we all still were, after three years in the presence of the Son of God! I felt deeply sorry for Thomas, and even more for the Lord who had put up with men like him . . . and me.

Some of us reproached Thomas; I tried arguing with him. Somehow, all this merely hardened him in his attitude.

For the next week he grew steadily more morose and irritable. Then, for the first time in a week, all eleven of us were together in that locked and barred upper room. Someone broached the subject of the evidences which our Lord had shown us for his Messiahship in the prophecies of Scripture. A discussion, ignored by Thomas, was developing when suddenly . . . there was the Lord, with the familiar Jewish greeting of peace.

Before we could even jump to our feet he was saying to Thomas, 'Reach your finger here! Examine my hands. Explore the wound in my side. Put your doubts to rest, and believe.'

Thomas, all bias gone, was on his knees at the feet of Jesus, worshipping and exclaiming, 'My Lord, and my God!'

The Lord commended him for his response, but at the same time gently reproved him for shutting his mind to faith.

'Because you have seen me, you believe. Blessed are those who never saw me, *yet believe!*'

I had learned a lesson — how to treat those whose faith is weak. Without impatience or argument, I would try to reveal my dear Lord Jesus to them as Sacrifice and Exemplar. Perhaps then they will utter those heavenly words, 'My Lord, and my God!'

Concluding testimony:

My death on Golgotha and my resurrection from Joseph's tomb had not changed me. Although I rose from the grave glorified in body, as all the saints will be after their resurrection, I was still Jesus of Nazareth, 'Son of Man' and 'Son of God', the same in character and spirit, forever yearning over the creatures I brought into existence.

So it was that from the shore I watched those seven men in their boat as they struggled all night long on the lake of Galilee and caught no fish. They talked of me and the things I did — the fierce storm on these waters, brought to an abrupt end; the more than ten thousand men and women who on the hillside over there were fed to satiety on an armful of food; the miracles of Capernaum where the wavelets lapped the shore . . . .

By the time dawn turned the skies grey they had drifted close to shore, and I hailed them with the words, 'Friends, have you caught nothing?'

'No,' the shadowy figures answered, backs to me.

'Cast your net on the right side of the boat, and you will make a catch!'

They hesitated, faced about towards me, set to work and soon could hardly handle the overfull net. The symbolism in facing my way — as they must do in all their future work — would eventually dawn on them.

'It's the Lord!' John shouted.

Peter, stripped for work to just something round his hips, grabbed an outer garment, threw it over himself, jumped overboard and came wading out to join me. The other six came in their boat, dragging the net, and exclaimed in surprise as they saw that I had bread for them and fish on a fire of coals.

'Bring out the fish you've caught,' I suggested, and Peter sprang to help. They counted the fish — one hundred and fifty-three, all large.

I served breakfast and they ate in awed silence, watching me, remembering the time when I called them from another miraculous catch to become fishers of men. What had just happened was intended to deepen that impression. I was renewing my commission to them. Facing the right way, executing my plans in my way, they were still to work for my kingdom, and I would provide for their needs.

Peter had disowned me. This was well known, and brought him the distrust of many and a severe crippling of his influence in spite of his repentance. I must help him to greater usefulness.

'Simon, son of Jonas,' I said to Peter, 'do you love me unswervingly — more than you love these men?'

Once he would have become excited and made fervent claims for the quality of his love. Now he was subdued, heartsore at the weakness he had displayed in Caiaphas's court, and anything but bursting with self-confidence.

'Yes, Lord, you know I love you.'

'Then feed my lambs' — those new in the faith.

He had disowned me three times, so I repeated, 'Simon, son of Jonas, do you love me unswervingly?'

He stared at the ground. 'Lord . . . yes, you know I love you.'

'Then tend my sheep.'

The silence was becoming uncomfortable when I asked the third time, 'Simon, son of Jonas, do you . . . love me?'

He shut his eyes against the pain of remembering. 'Lord, you know everything. You know I love you,' he whispered.

This was a new Peter, as the others could see. I had recommissioned him; and in the process had underlined that the supreme condition in following me and working for me is *love*, unswerving and high-principled.

A little later I took him aside, to strengthen him for what lay ahead.

'Before age catches up with you, you are used to tying your belt about you and going where you please. Now listen carefully. When age comes, you will stretch out your arms.' I met his gaze intently. I was predicting his crucifixion, as he would later realize. Hours before my crucifixion he protested that he would follow me anywhere, and I answered, 'Not now — you will, *later*.'

As we walked on I continued, 'Then, a stranger will tie you up. You will be taken to a place not of your own choosing.' He was beginning to understand; and to this man who tended to rush ahead of my providences, I offered a sterling rule, '*Follow* me!'

Moments later he glanced over his shoulder and saw John following us. At once he wanted to know what the future held for this man.

'Suppose I wanted him to stay till I return — what business is that of yours? *Your* business is to follow me.'

I had not put him in charge of John or any other of his brothers. He was not a lord over God's heritage. If he faithfully and humbly followed me, the Chief Shepherd, I would give him the crown of life . . . as I would any other soul who put himself into my hands.

Before my death I made an appointment with my disciples: 'After I have risen, I will go ahead of you to Galilee.' Galilee, where I had worked most fruitfully and had more believers than anywhere else, and where the priests had less power to interfere in our comings and goings. The disciples knew the date of the appointment, and the mountain where they would meet. After my resurrection I reminded them three times of the arrangement.

The story spread, and on the designated date about five hundred believers and their friends converged on the mountainside from all directions, and as they waited in eager groups my disciples moved about, relating what had happened on the lake.

Suddenly I stood among them. Nearly all fell down in worship. Those who knew me were aware of the miracles, my authority over evil spirits and the elements of nature. They hoped, especially now that I was alive once more, that I would set up my throne in Jerusalem. In what I was about to announce, they and the world must see the infinitely greater scope of my work.

'All authority has been given to me — all authority in heaven and on earth!'

Not authority in Jerusalem, mere power over the nation; but boundless power and authority, transcending time and space.

'In view of this, I charge you to go and make disciples in all nations. Teach them to obey everything I have commanded you. Baptize them in the name of the Father, the Son, and the Holy Spirit. I will sustain you in this, to the very end of history!'

The Jewish nation had failed me, elevating human traditions to church law. You must not fail me. Go, and let your message be what I have taught through prophets of old, by my personal teaching, and by my example.

I could not let five hundred people travel, some for days, to hear me speak on this hill — and then dismiss them after two minutes. I therefore taught them about the kingdom: I had not come to establish a temporal kingdom, but a spiritual one. As I had done on the way to Emmaus, I opened the Scriptures for the five hundred, explaining my substitutionary death and the whole plan of salvation, and urging them to study the Scriptures far more earnestly.

They were to start their witnessing in Jerusalem, no matter what persecution they had to face; and from there go to earth's remotest bounds. The Holy Spirit would be my presence to them, and my enabling power. Wherever necessary, in the wisdom of the Spirit, miraculous power would attend their work. The main miracle would be the life transformed, recreated in God's image. Convincing objective evidence of the work of the true Spirit would be the fruits of the Spirit, and 'obedience to everything I have commanded you.'

The five hundred — who would soon see thousands converted in one day, even in difficult Jerusalem — now had their commission and their message . . . and knew who their Commander was.

As a result of the meeting with the five hundred, my brothers, James, Joses, Simon and Jude, who came to see their killed-yet-alive brother, became believers. Later I met with James again, because of his great potential as leader in the young church.

Now my eleven disciples went to Jerusalem to start their witnessing. I met them there and took them for what they did not know would be our last walk. Down the Kidron, past Gethsemane and up Olivet to near Bethany we went, and all the time I talked earnestly, reminding them of things I had previously said, the things that to my Father and me were *truth:* for truth matters to me very, very much.

We halted. I had said everything I wanted to say. It was time to go, but looking into these dear weather-beaten faces I could hardly tear myself away. How many days we had spent together, praying, talking, working! How well I knew them, how dearly I loved them! How readily had they given up ease, security, and loved ones to follow me!

Oh, Father, bless these dear men . . . .

'My Father bless you, dear friends.'

I raise my hands in blessing, see shock and surprise in their eyes as I slowly ascend. I stare down at my precious friends until the clouds of angels enclose me to escort me to my Father, and at once send two down to comfort them.

The brilliant beings ask them, 'Men of Galilee, why stand staring up into the sky? This very same Jesus, who has been taken away from you up to heaven, will return in the same way as you have seen him go!'

Have faith! I go to prepare a place for you. When all is ready I will come again to take you to where I am, in the presence of the ever-loving Father.

BIBLICAL REFERENCES

1 Matt. 26:36-56; Mark 14:32-52; Luke 22:40-53; John 18:1-12.
2 Luke 2; Matt. 2; Gen. 3:15; Micah 5:2; Num. 24:17.
3 Luke 2.
4 Matt. 2; Jer. 9:23, 24; 1 Kings 19:11, 12; John 7:15; Luke 2:39-49; Gen. 22; Luke 1:26-38; Exod. 12; Zech. 3:3, 4; Isa. 1:11, 14; Isa. 52:13, 14, 53:3, 7-12; Deut. 18:15-18; Micah 6:6-8; Heb. 10:1-4; Isa. 1:11.
5 Matt. 3:1-12; Mark 1:1-8; Luke 3:1-18; Isa. 40:3-5; Mal. 3:1; Luke 1:5-25, 39-45; Dan. 9:25-27; Luke 3:15.
6 Matt. 3:11-17; Luke 3:21-23a; Mark 1:9-11; Exod. 3:5; Luke 1:36.
7 Matt. 4:1-11; Mark 1:12, 13; Luke 4:1-13; Rev. 12:7; Isa. 14:12-14; Ezek. 28:13-17; Heb. 2:14; Phil. 2:6, 7; John 8:28, 5:30; Heb. 9:14, 15, 4:15; Luke 4:1; Isa. 52:14; Deut. 8:3; Ps. 91:11, 12; Deut. 6:16; Dan. 4:17; Deut. 6:13.
8 John 1:19-51; Isa. 40:3.
9 John 2:1-12; Prov. 20:1, 23:31, 32; James 1:17.
10 John 2:13-25; Exod. 29:38-42; Num. 28:3-8; 1 Cor. 10:4; Col. 1:16; 1 Sam. 15:22, 23; Ps. 50:13; Isa. 1:11; Rev. 17; Isa. 55:1; Ps. 69:9; Mal. 3:1, 2.
11 John 3:1-21.
12 John 3:22-36.
13 John 4:1-42; Deut. 18:15, 18; Gen. 49:10, 17:19, 3:15; Gal. 3:16; Deut. 34:10; Isa. 9:6; Matt. 12:6, 41, 42.
14 John 4:43-54; Zech. 6:13; Phil. 2:5-8; Heb. 5:7-9; John 3:34; Matt. 4:1.
15 John 5:1-47; Gen. 49:10; Isa. 9:2, 6; Isa. 1:13, 14; Isa. 10:1, 1:15.
16 Luke 3:19, 20; Matt. 14:3-5, 4:12; Mark 1:14, 15; Luke 4:14, 15; Amos 3:7; Deut. 29:29.
17 Luke 4:16-30; Jer. 23:5, 6, 33:17; Gen. 49:10; Isa. 61:1, 2, 58:6; Ps. 132:11, 12; Isa. 1:4, 9:7; Eccl. 3:1; 1 Kings 17:8-24, 18:1; James 5:17; 2 Kings 5:1-19; Luke 4:31a.
18 Luke 5:1-11; Mark 1:16-20; Matt. 4:18-22.
19 Matt. 4:13-17; Mark 1:21-28; Luke 4:31b-37; Mark 1:29-39; Matt. 8:14-17; Luke 4:38-44; Matt. 4:23-25; Isa. 42:2.
20 Acts 9; Mark 1:40-45; Matt. 8:2-4; Luke 5:12-16.
21 Mark 2:1-12; Matt. 9:2-8; Luke 5:17-26.
22 Mark 2:13, 14; Matt. 9:9; Luke 5:27, 28.
23 Mark 2:23-28; Matt. 12:1-8; Luke 6:1-5; Hosea 6:6.
24 Mark 3:1-6; Luke 6:6-11; Matt. 12:9-14; Isa. 56:1, 2.
25 Mark 3:7-19; Matt. 12:15-21; Luke 6:12-49; Matt. 5:1-8:1; Ps. 40:8.

26   Matt. 5:14, 6:1-8:1.
27   Luke 7:1-10; Matt. 8:5-13.
28   Matt. 9:27-34.
29   Luke 8:1-3; Matt. 9:35; Luke 7:11-17.
30   Matt. 12:46-13:23; Mark 3:31-4:20; Luke 8:19-21, 4-15; Isa. 6:9, 10.
31   Matt. 13:24-53; Mark 4:21-34; Luke 8:16-18; Song of Solomon 5:10; John 17:3; 1 John 5:11, 12; Luke 13:20, 21.
32   Matt. 8:18-22; Matt. 8:18, 23-27; Mark 4:35-41; Luke 8:22-25; John 5:19.
33   Mark 5:1-20; Matt. 8:28-9:1; Luke 8:26-39.
34   Mark 5:21-43; Matt. 9:18-26; Luke 8:40-56.
35   Luke 7:18-23; Matt. 11:2-6; Isa. 61:1, 8:14; Rom. 9:32, 33; Matt. 11:7-30; Luke 7:24-35; Mal. 3:1 (Isa. 40:3-5; Mal. 4:5, 6); Eccl. 10:17; Prov. 23:2, 31, 32, 20:1; Ps. 40:8; John 6:38.
36   Matt. 9:36-11:1; Mark 6:7-13; Luke 9:1-6.
37   Mark 6:1-6, 14-29; Matt. 13:54-58, 14:1, 2, 6-12; Luke 9:7-9.
38   Mark 6:30-44; John 6:1-14; Matt. 14:13-21; Luke 9:10-17.
39   Matt. 14:22-36; John 6:15-24; Mark 6:45-56.
40   John 6:25-7:1; Isa. 54:13.
41   Matt. 15:21-28; Mark 7:24-30.
42   Mark 7:31-37; Matt. 15:29-31.
43   Matt. 15:32-39; Mark 8:1-10.
44   Matt. 16:13-28; Mark 8:27-9:1; Luke 9:18-27; John 1:49; Rev. 21:14; Luke 11:52; Matt. 18:18; Mark 7:7, 21-23; Mal. 3:6; Heb. 13:8; Mark 1:24; Luke 4:34.
45   Mark 9:30-32; Matt. 17:22, 23; Luke 9:43b-45; Matt. 17:1-13; Mark 9:2-13; Luke 9:28-36.
46   Mark 9:14-29; Matt. 17:14-21; Luke 9:37-43a; Mal. 3:1, 4:5; Isa. 53; 'in my name' as in Matt. 7:21-23; Rev. 16:14; Matt. 7:23.
47   Matt. 17:24-27, 18:1-35; Mark 9:33-50; Luke 9:46-50; 1 Cor. 7:19; Mal. 3:6.
48   John 7:2-31; Isa. 53:1; Rev. 19:11-16.
49   John 7:32-52; Isa. 24:23; Jer. 8:20; Exod. 17:6.
50   John 7:53-8:11.
51   John 8:12-59.
52   John 9:1-41; John 10:1-21; Jer. 31:3.
53   Luke 10:25-37.
54   Luke 10:38-42, 17-24; Rev. 12:7-9, 20:15, 21:27.
55   John 10:22-42, 11:1-13.
56   Luke 13:31-35, 9:7-9, 18:9-14; Acts 6:7; Luke 15:1-7, 8-10, 11-32.
57   John 11:1-45.
58   John 11:46-57; Luke 17:11-19.
59   Luke 18:1-8; Matt. 19:3-12; Mark 10:2-12; Matt. 19:16-30; Mark

10:17-31; Luke 18:18-30; Col. 1:16, 17; John 1:1-3; 1 Cor. 10:4; Neh. 9:13, 14; Matt. 20:1-16.

60   Mark 10:46-52; Matt. 20:29-34; Luke 18:35-43; Luke 19:1-10.

61   Luke 19:11-28; Matt. 26:6-13; Luke 7:36-50; Mark 14:3-9; John 11:55-57, 12:1-9.

62   Matt. 21:1-11, 17; Mark 11:1-11; Luke 19:29-44; John 12:12-19; Zech. 9:9.

63   Mark 11:12-14, 20-26, 15-19; Matt. 21:18-22, 12-17; Luke 19:45-48; Isa. 56:7; Jer. 7:11; Ps. 8:2; Matt. 21:23-46; Mark 12:1-12; Luke 20:9-19; Ps. 118:22, 23.

64   Matt. 22:1-14; Matt. 22:15-33; Mark 12:13-27; Luke 20:20-38; Exod. 3:6, 16; Mark 12:28-37; Matt. 22:34-46; Luke 20:39-44; Deut. 6:5; Lev. 19:18; Ps. 110:1; Acts 2:34; Heb. 1:13; Matt. 23:1-39; Mark 12:38-40; Luke 20:45-47; Rev. 1:7; Matt. 24:30; Phil. 2:9-11; Mark 12:41-44; Luke 21:1-4; John 12:20-36a; John 12:37-50, 36b.

65   Matt. 24:1-51; Mark 13:1-37; Luke 21:5-38; Dan. 11:31.

66   Matt. 25:1-13, 14-30, 31-46; John 16:2.

67   Matt. 26:2, 17-20; Mark 14:12-18a; Luke 22:7-16, 24-30; John 13:1-20; Phil. 2:6, 7.

68   Heb. 9:15-17; Lev. 23; Matt. 26:26-29, 21-25; Mark 14:22-25, 18b-21; Luke 22:17-20, 21-23.

69   John 13:31-14:31; Lev. 19:18; Mark 1:24; Matt. 7:21-23, 26:30; John 14:31; Ps. 117:1, 2.

70   Luke 22:39, 31-38; Mark 14:26, 27-31; Matt. 26:31-35, and chapter 10; Zech. 13:7; Isa. 53:12; John 15:1-16:33, 17:1-26.

71   Matt. 26:36-56; Mark 14:32-52; Luke 22:40-53; John 18:1-12, 15:10, 6:38; Zech. 13:7.

72   John 18:13-24, 2:19; Matt. 5:39, 26:57-75, 10:32, 27:3-10, 26:67, 68, 27:1; Mark 14:53-15:1; Luke 22:54-71; Isa. 53:7.

73   John 18:28-38; Luke 23:1-5; Matt. 27:2, 11-14; Mark 15:2-5.

74   Luke 23:6-25; Matt. 27:15-31a; John 18:39-19:16; Mark 15:6-19.

75   Matt. 20:18, 26:2, 31, 27:31b-56, 21:9; Mark 14:27, 15:20-41; John 16:32, 19:17-37; Luke 23:26-49; James 4:17; John 9:41; Ps. 22:18; Rev. 2:7, 22:1; Luke 23:43, translation by Lamsa from the Eastern Text, publ. A. J. Holman Company, Philadelphia, 1940: 'Jesus said to him, Truly I say to you today, you will be with me in Paradise.' The original Greek had no punctuation. It reads: *amēn soi legō sēmeron met emou esē en tō paradeisō*, literally, 'truly to-you I-say today with-me you-will-be in the paradise.' The adverb *sēmeron*, 'today', stands between the two verbs *legō*, 'I-say', and *esē*, 'you-will-be', and might apply to either. In view of the fact that 'paradise' is obviously synonymous with 'heaven' where God's throne is (2 Cor. 12:2-4; Rev. 2:7, 21:1-3, 10,

and had not realize
how often these were
so weary. I'm glad I
was able to go to the holy
land when y did, as y
know how hot some of the
places must have been
think you a going love freda

Sat 14

Dear Christine

Thank you very much
for the book, I found
it very easy reading
and very interesting
see thing from a

22:1-5), and in the light of John 20:17, the author prefers to associate the adverb 'today' with the verb 'I-say' immediately preceding it. Isa. 53:12.

76 Matt. 27:50-66; Mark 15:38-47; Luke 23:47-56; John 19:31-42, 16:32; Heb. 10:1-10; 2 Cor. 5:19; Rev. 20:7-15; Exod. 12:46; Zech. 12:10; Ps. 2.

77 Matt. 28:1-15; John 20:1-18, 11:25; Mark 16:1-11; Luke 24:1-12; Isa. 26:19.

78 Luke 24:13-49; 1 Cor. 15:3-6; Col. 1:16, 17; Luke 24:33-49; John 20:19-23; Mark 16:12, 13; John 20:24-29; Mark 16:14; John 21:1-23; Matt. 28:16-20; Mark 16:15-18; Acts 15; Luke 24:50-53; Mark 16:19, 20.